FLORIDA STATE PARKS BUCKET JOURNAL

Visit the state parks and historic sites of Florida, USA

This book belongs to

_____

If found please call

_____

In 1944, the park service defined its objective, which was "**to save … unspoiled Florida scenery** for the use and enjoyment of future generations, to provide healthful outdoor recreation, promote conservation of wildlife and other natural resources, encourage education and travel and altogether make Florida a better place in which to live."

"**When people ask how close to the beach I am**, I say, "12 minutes or 12 hours. Depends on which beach you want to go to." ~ Jarod Kintz

"**You can shake the sand** from your shoes but not from your soul." ~Unknown

D1478116

FLORIDA STATE PARKS BUCKET JOURNAL

Disclaimer
The information in this book is based on the author's opinion, knowledge and experience. The publisher and the author will not be held liable for the use or misuse of the information contained herein.

Disclosure
This book may contain affiliate links. If you click through an affiliate link to a third-party website and make a purchase, the author may receive a small commission.

ISBN: 978-1-63933-016-4
Publisher: My Bucket Journals, LLC, PO Box 310, Hutto TX 78634

You are a sun loving Floridian; a traveler, adventurer, and freedom lover who wants to experience your state and remember it.

In this Florida State Parks Bucket Journal, you will find pages for each of the **186 state parks, recreation areas, and preserves**.

This bucket journal is different. It gives you the ability to create your own unique exploration of whichever state park or historic site you choose

How to Use Your Florida State Parks Bucket Journal

Parks that offer *camping or other overnight accommodations* are on orange pages.

❑ Search out details about the state park or recreational site by using the website URL provided.

❑ Have fun planning the things you want to see on the left side of the 2-page spread.

❑ This is best done before you take your trip, but can be done while you are out exploring.

❑ On the right side, chronicle everything that you do and experience. Included is space for reflection about your stay in the park.

Parks that are *Day Use Area Only* are on tan pages.

❑ Day use parks are still fun to visit, even if you can't sleep there.
❑ Visit them when you are staying at other overnight parks or use them as day trip excursions to get out and explore.

This Florida State Parks Bucket Journal will become a living memory of your trips and adventures as you discover the wonders of the State of Florida. Years from now you'll look back at this journal with fondness, remembering the friends and family that made these trips a treasure.

TABLE OF PARKS

TABLE OF PARKS

ASP: *Archaeological State Park* HSP: *Historic State Park* PSP: *Preserve State Park* SP: *State Park*

TABLE OF PARKS

APSP: *Archaeological Preserve State Park* GSP: *Geological State Park* HSP: *Historic State Park* PSP: *Preserve State Park* SP: *State Park*

TABLE OF PARKS

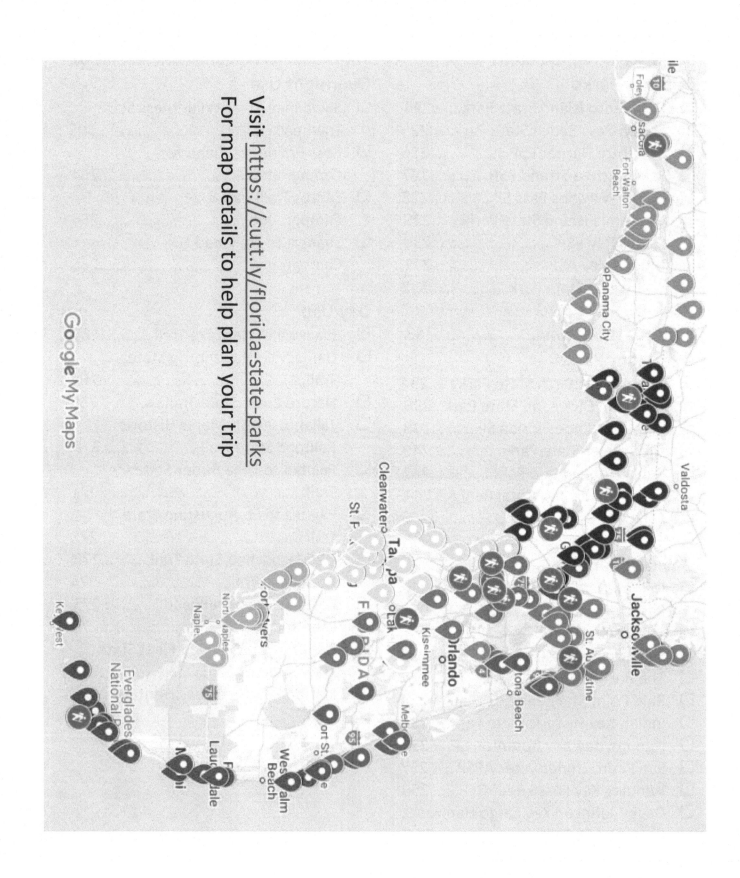

Visit https://cutt.ly/florida-state-parks

For map details to help plan your trip

Google My Maps

8

Northwest

- Bay
- Escambia
- Franklin
- Gulf
- Holmes
- Jackson
- Liberty
- Okaloosa
- Santa Rosa
- Walton
- Washington

Camp Helen State Park
City: Panama City Beach   County: Bay

Plan your trip https://www.floridastateparks.org/index.php/parks-and-trails/camp-helen-state-park

Activities:

- ❑ Beach Access
- ❑ Biking Trails
- ❑ Boating
- ❑ Campfire
- ❑ Caving
- ❑ Disc Golf
- ❑ Fishing
- ❑ Geo Cache
- ❑ Golf
- ❑ Hiking
- ❑ Horseback

- ❑ Hunting
- ❑ OHV
- ❑ Park Tours
- ❑ Rock Climbing
- ❑ Snorkeling
- ❑ Stargazing
- ❑ Swimming
- ❑ Viewpoint
- ❑ Wildlife & Birding
- ❑
- ❑

Facilities:

- ❑ ADA
- ❑ Gym
- ❑ Historic Sites
- ❑ Lodge
- ❑ Meeting Hall
- ❑ Pavilions
- ❑ Picnic sites
- ❑ Pool
- ❑ Restrooms

- ❑ Showers
- ❑ Visitor Center
- ❑ RV Camp
- ❑ Tent Camp
- ❑ Cabins
- ❑ Lodge Rooms
- ❑
- ❑
- ❑

Notes:

Get the Facts

- ❑ Phone: 850-233-5059
- ❑ Park Hours

  _____

- ❑ Reservations? ____Y ____N

  date made_____

- ❑ Open year 'round ___Y___N

  dates_____

- ❑ Check in time _____
- ❑ Check out time _____
- ❑ Dog friendly _____Y _____N
- ❑ Max RV length _____
- ❑ Distance from home

  miles: _____

  hours: _____

- ❑ Address_____

  _____

  _____

Fees:

- ❑ Day Use $ _____
- ❑ Camp Sites $_____
- ❑ RV Sites $ _____
- ❑ Refund policy

  _____

  _____

  _____

Make It Personal

Trip dates: _____

Why I went: _____

I went with: _____

How I got there: (circle all that apply) Plane   Train   Car   Bus   Bike   Hike   RV   MC

We stayed in (space, cabin, etc.) _____

_____

The weather was: Sunny   Cloudy   Rainy   Stormy   Snowy   Foggy   Warm   Cold

Most relaxing day: _____

_____

Something funny: _____

_____

Someone we met: _____

_____

Best story told: _____

_____

The kids liked this: _____

The best food: _____

_____

Games played: _____

_____

Something disappointing: _____

_____

Next time I'll do this differently: _____

_____

St. Andrews State Park
City: Panama City Beach   County: Bay

Plan your trip https://www.floridastateparks.org/parks-and-trails/st-andrews-state-park

Activities:

- ❑ Beach Access
- ❑ Biking Trails
- ❑ Boating
- ❑ Campfire
- ❑ Caving
- ❑ Disc Golf
- ❑ Fishing
- ❑ Geo Cache
- ❑ Golf
- ❑ Hiking
- ❑ Horseback

- ❑ Hunting
- ❑ OHV
- ❑ Park Tours
- ❑ Rock Climbing
- ❑ Snorkeling
- ❑ Stargazing
- ❑ Swimming
- ❑ Viewpoint
- ❑ Wildlife & Birding
- ❑
- ❑

Facilities:

- ❑ ADA
- ❑ Gym
- ❑ Historic Sites
- ❑ Lodge
- ❑ Meeting Hall
- ❑ Pavilions
- ❑ Picnic sites
- ❑ Pool
- ❑ Restrooms

- ❑ Showers
- ❑ Visitor Center
- ❑ RV Camp
- ❑ Tent Camp
- ❑ Cabins
- ❑ Lodge Rooms
- ❑
- ❑
- ❑

Notes:

Get the Facts

- ❑ Phone: 850-708-6100
- ❑ Park Hours

   _____

- ❑ Reservations? ____Y ____N

   date made_____

- ❑ Open year 'round ___Y___N

   dates_____

- ❑ Check in time _____
- ❑ Check out time _____
- ❑ Dog friendly _____Y _____N
- ❑ Max RV length _____
- ❑ Distance from home

   miles: _____

   hours: _____

- ❑ Address_____

   _____

   _____

Fees:

- ❑ Day Use $ _____
- ❑ Camp Sites $_____
- ❑ RV Sites $ _____
- ❑ Refund policy

   _____

   _____

   _____

Make It Personal

Trip dates: _____

Why I went: _____

I went with: _____

How I got there: (circle all that apply) Plane   Train   Car   Bus   Bike   Hike   RV   MC

We stayed in (space, cabin, etc.) _____

_____

The weather was: Sunny   Cloudy   Rainy   Stormy   Snowy   Foggy   Warm   Cold

Most relaxing day: _____

_____

Something funny: _____

_____

Someone we met: _____

_____

Best story told: _____

_____

The kids liked this: _____

The best food: _____

Games played: _____

Something disappointing: _____

Next time I'll do this differently: _____

_____

Big Lagoon State Park
City: Pensacola   County: Escambia

Plan your trip: https://www.floridastateparks.org/parks-and-trails/big-lagoon-state-park

Activities:

- ❏ Beach Access
- ❏ Biking Trails
- ❏ Boating
- ❏ Campfire
- ❏ Caving
- ❏ Disc Golf
- ❏ Fishing
- ❏ Geo Cache
- ❏ Golf
- ❏ Hiking
- ❏ Horseback

- ❏ Hunting
- ❏ OHV
- ❏ Park Tours
- ❏ Rock Climbing
- ❏ Snorkeling
- ❏ Stargazing
- ❏ Swimming
- ❏ Viewpoint
- ❏ Wildlife & Birding
- ❏
- ❏

Facilities:

- ❏ ADA
- ❏ Gym
- ❏ Historic Sites
- ❏ Lodge
- ❏ Meeting Hall
- ❏ Pavilions
- ❏ Picnic sites
- ❏ Pool
- ❏ Restrooms

- ❏ Showers
- ❏ Visitor Center
- ❏ RV Camp
- ❏ Tent Camp
- ❏ Cabins
- ❏ Lodge Rooms
- ❏
- ❏
- ❏

Notes:

Get the Facts

- ❏ Phone: 850-492-1595
- ❏ Park Hours

  _____

- ❏ Reservations? ____Y ____N

  date made_____

- ❏ Open year 'round ___Y___N

  dates_____

- ❏ Check in time _____
- ❏ Check out time _____
- ❏ Dog friendly _____Y _____N
- ❏ Max RV length _____
- ❏ Distance from home

  miles: _____

  hours: _____

- ❏ Address_____

  _____

  _____

Fees:

- ❏ Day Use $ _____
- ❏ Camp Sites $_____
- ❏ RV Sites $ _____
- ❏ Refund policy

  _____

  _____

  _____

Make It Personal

Trip dates: _____

Why I went: _____

I went with: _____

How I got there: (circle all that apply) Plane Train Car Bus Bike Hike RV MC

We stayed in (space, cabin, etc.)
_____

The weather was: Sunny Cloudy Rainy Stormy Snowy Foggy Warm Cold

Most relaxing day: _____
_____

Something funny: _____
_____

Someone we met: _____
_____

Best story told: _____
_____

The kids liked this: _____

The best food: _____

Games played: _____

_____

Something disappointing: _____

_____

Next time I'll do this differently: __

_____

Dr. Julian G. Bruce St. George Island SP
City: St George Island   County: Franklin

Plan your Trip https://www.floridastateparks.org/parks-and-trails/dr-julian-g-bruce-st-george-island-state-park

Activities:

- ❑ Beach Access
- ❑ Biking Trails
- ❑ Boating
- ❑ Campfire
- ❑ Caving
- ❑ Disc Golf
- ❑ Fishing
- ❑ Geo Cache
- ❑ Golf
- ❑ Hiking
- ❑ Horseback

- ❑ Hunting
- ❑ OHV
- ❑ Park Tours
- ❑ Rock Climbing
- ❑ Snorkeling
- ❑ Stargazing
- ❑ Swimming
- ❑ Viewpoint
- ❑ Wildlife & Birding
- ❑
- ❑

Facilities:

- ❑ ADA
- ❑ Gym
- ❑ Historic Sites
- ❑ Lodge
- ❑ Meeting Hall
- ❑ Pavilions
- ❑ Picnic sites
- ❑ Pool
- ❑ Restrooms

- ❑ Showers
- ❑ Visitor Center
- ❑ RV Camp
- ❑ Tent Camp
- ❑ Cabins
- ❑ Lodge Rooms
- ❑
- ❑
- ❑

Notes:

Get the Facts

- ❑ Phone: 850-927-2111
- ❑ Park Hours

   _____

- ❑ Reservations? ____Y ____N

   date made_____

- ❑ Open year 'round ___Y__N

   dates_____

- ❑ Check in time _____
- ❑ Check out time _____
- ❑ Dog friendly _____Y _____N
- ❑ Max RV length _____
- ❑ Distance from home

   miles: _____

   hours: _____

- ❑ Address_____

   _____

   _____

Fees:

- ❑ Day Use $ _____
- ❑ Camp Sites $_____
- ❑ RV Sites $ _____
- ❑ Refund policy

   _____

   _____

   _____

Make It Personal

Trip dates:

Why I went:

I went with:

How I got there: (circle all that apply) Plane   Train   Car   Bus   Bike   Hike   RV   MC

We stayed in (space, cabin, etc.)

The weather was: Sunny   Cloudy   Rainy   Stormy   Snowy   Foggy   Warm   Cold

Most relaxing day:

Something funny:

Someone we met:

Best story told:

The kids liked this:

The best food:

Games played:

Something disappointing:

Next time I'll do this differently:

T.H. Stone Memorial St. Joseph Peninsula SP
City: Port St. Joe   County: Gulf

Plan your trip https://www.floridastateparks.org/parks-and-trails/th-stone-memorial-st-joseph-peninsula-state-park

Activities:

- ❑ Beach Access
- ❑ Biking Trails
- ❑ Boating
- ❑ Campfire
- ❑ Caving
- ❑ Disc Golf
- ❑ Fishing
- ❑ Geo Cache
- ❑ Golf
- ❑ Hiking
- ❑ Horseback

- ❑ Hunting
- ❑ OHV
- ❑ Park Tours
- ❑ Rock Climbing
- ❑ Snorkeling
- ❑ Stargazing
- ❑ Swimming
- ❑ Viewpoint
- ❑ Wildlife & Birding
- ❑
- ❑

Facilities:

- ❑ ADA
- ❑ Gym
- ❑ Historic Sites
- ❑ Lodge
- ❑ Meeting Hall
- ❑ Pavilions
- ❑ Picnic sites
- ❑ Pool
- ❑ Restrooms

- ❑ Showers
- ❑ Visitor Center
- ❑ RV Camp
- ❑ Tent Camp
- ❑ Cabins
- ❑ Lodge Rooms
- ❑
- ❑
- ❑

Notes:

Get the Facts

- ❑ Phone: 850-227-1327
- ❑ Park Hours

  _____

- ❑ Reservations? ____Y ____N

  date made_____

- ❑ Open year 'round ___Y___N

  dates_____

- ❑ Check in time _____
- ❑ Check out time _____
- ❑ Dog friendly _____Y _____N
- ❑ Max RV length _____
- ❑ Distance from home

  miles: _____

  hours: _____

- ❑ Address_____

  _____

  _____

Fees:

- ❑ Day Use $ _____
- ❑ Camp Sites $_____
- ❑ RV Sites $ _____
- ❑ Refund policy

  _____

  _____

  _____

Make It Personal

Trip dates:

Why I went:

I went with:

How I got there: (circle all that apply) Plane   Train   Car   Bus   Bike   Hike   RV   MC

We stayed in (space, cabin, etc.)

The weather was: Sunny   Cloudy   Rainy   Stormy   Snowy   Foggy   Warm   Cold

Most relaxing day:

Something funny:

Someone we met:

Best story told:

The kids liked this:

The best food:

Games played:

Something disappointing:

Next time I'll do this differently:

Florida Caverns State Park
City: Marianna   County: Jackson

Plan your trip https://www.floridastateparks.org/parks-and-trails/florida-caverns-state-park

Activities:

- ❑ Beach Access
- ❑ Biking Trails
- ❑ Boating
- ❑ Campfire
- ❑ Caving
- ❑ Disc Golf
- ❑ Fishing
- ❑ Geo Cache
- ❑ Golf
- ❑ Hiking
- ❑ Horseback

- ❑ Hunting
- ❑ OHV
- ❑ Park Tours
- ❑ Rock Climbing
- ❑ Snorkeling
- ❑ Stargazing
- ❑ Swimming
- ❑ Viewpoint
- ❑ Wildlife & Birding
- ❑
- ❑

Facilities:

- ❑ ADA
- ❑ Gym
- ❑ Historic Sites
- ❑ Lodge
- ❑ Meeting Hall
- ❑ Pavilions
- ❑ Picnic sites
- ❑ Pool
- ❑ Restrooms

- ❑ Showers
- ❑ Visitor Center
- ❑ RV Camp
- ❑ Tent Camp
- ❑ Cabins
- ❑ Lodge Rooms
- ❑
- ❑
- ❑

Notes:

Get the Facts

- ❑ Phone: 850-482-1228
- ❑ Park Hours

  _____

- ❑ Reservations? ____Y ____N

  date made_____

- ❑ Open year 'round ___Y___N

  dates_____

- ❑ Check in time _____
- ❑ Check out time _____
- ❑ Dog friendly _____Y _____N
- ❑ Max RV length _____
- ❑ Distance from home

  miles: _____

  hours: _____

- ❑ Address_____

  _____

  _____

Fees:

- ❑ Day Use $ _____
- ❑ Camp Sites $_____
- ❑ RV Sites $ _____
- ❑ Refund policy

  _____

  _____

  _____

Make It Personal

Trip dates:

Why I went:

I went with:

How I got there: (circle all that apply) Plane   Train   Car   Bus   Bike   Hike   RV   MC

We stayed in (space, cabin, etc.)

The weather was: Sunny   Cloudy   Rainy   Stormy   Snowy   Foggy   Warm   Cold

Most relaxing day:

Something funny:

Someone we met:

Best story told:

The kids liked this:

The best food:

Games played:

Something disappointing:

Next time I'll do this differently:

Three Rivers State Park
City: Sneads   County: Jackson

Plan your trip https://www.floridastateparks.org/parks-and-trails/three-rivers-state-park

Activities:

- ❑ Beach Access
- ❑ Biking Trails
- ❑ Boating
- ❑ Campfire
- ❑ Caving
- ❑ Disc Golf
- ❑ Fishing
- ❑ Geo Cache
- ❑ Golf
- ❑ Hiking
- ❑ Horseback

- ❑ Hunting
- ❑ OHV
- ❑ Park Tours
- ❑ Rock Climbing
- ❑ Snorkeling
- ❑ Stargazing
- ❑ Swimming
- ❑ Viewpoint
- ❑ Wildlife & Birding
- ❑
- ❑

Facilities:

- ❑ ADA
- ❑ Gym
- ❑ Historic Sites
- ❑ Lodge
- ❑ Meeting Hall
- ❑ Pavilions
- ❑ Picnic sites
- ❑ Pool
- ❑ Restrooms

- ❑ Showers
- ❑ Visitor Center
- ❑ RV Camp
- ❑ Tent Camp
- ❑ Cabins
- ❑ Lodge Rooms
- ❑
- ❑
- ❑

Notes:

Get the Facts

- ❑ Phone: 850-482-9006
- ❑ Park Hours

  _____

- ❑ Reservations? ____Y ____N

  date made_____

- ❑ Open year 'round ___Y___N

  dates_____

- ❑ Check in time _____

- ❑ Check out time _____

- ❑ Dog friendly _____Y _____N

- ❑ Max RV length _____

- ❑ Distance from home

  miles: _____

  hours: _____

- ❑ Address_____

  _____

  _____

Fees:

- ❑ Day Use $ _____
- ❑ Camp Sites $_____
- ❑ RV Sites $ _____
- ❑ Refund policy

  _____

  _____

  _____

Make It Personal

Trip dates: _____

Why I went: _____

I went with: _____

How I got there: (circle all that apply) Plane   Train   Car   Bus   Bike   Hike   RV   MC

We stayed in (space, cabin, etc.) _____
_____

The weather was: Sunny Cloudy Rainy Stormy Snowy Foggy Warm Cold

Most relaxing day: _____
_____

Something funny: _____
_____

Someone we met: _____
_____

Best story told: _____
_____

The kids liked this: _____

The best food: _____
_____

Games played: _____

_____

Something disappointing: _____

_____

Next time I'll do this differently: _____

_____

23

Torreya State Park
City: Bristol   County: Liberty

Plan your Trip https://www.floridastateparks.org/index.php/parks-and-trails/torreya-state-park

Activities:

- ❑ Beach Access
- ❑ Biking Trails
- ❑ Boating
- ❑ Campfire
- ❑ Caving
- ❑ Disc Golf
- ❑ Fishing
- ❑ Geo Cache
- ❑ Golf
- ❑ Hiking
- ❑ Horseback

- ❑ Hunting
- ❑ OHV
- ❑ Park Tours
- ❑ Rock Climbing
- ❑ Snorkeling
- ❑ Stargazing
- ❑ Swimming
- ❑ Viewpoint
- ❑ Wildlife & Birding
- ❑
- ❑

Facilities:

- ❑ ADA
- ❑ Gym
- ❑ Historic Sites
- ❑ Lodge
- ❑ Meeting Hall
- ❑ Pavilions
- ❑ Picnic sites
- ❑ Pool
- ❑ Restrooms

- ❑ Showers
- ❑ Visitor Center
- ❑ RV Camp
- ❑ Tent Camp
- ❑ Cabins
- ❑ Lodge Rooms
- ❑
- ❑
- ❑

Notes:

Get the Facts

- ❑ Phone: 850-643-2674
- ❑ Park Hours

  _____

- ❑ Reservations? ____Y ____N

  date made_____

- ❑ Open year 'round ___Y___N

  dates_____

- ❑ Check in time _____

- ❑ Check out time _____

- ❑ Dog friendly _____Y _____N

- ❑ Max RV length _____

- ❑ Distance from home

  miles: _____

  hours: _____

- ❑ Address_____

  _____

  _____

Fees:

- ❑ Day Use $ _____
- ❑ Camp Sites $_____
- ❑ RV Sites $ _____
- ❑ Refund policy

  _____

  _____

  _____

Make It Personal

Trip dates: _____

Why I went: _____

I went with: _____

How I got there: (circle all that apply) Plane   Train   Car   Bus   Bike   Hike   RV   MC

We stayed in (space, cabin, etc.) _____

_____

The weather was: Sunny   Cloudy   Rainy   Stormy   Snowy   Foggy   Warm   Cold

Most relaxing day: _____

_____

Something funny: _____

_____

Someone we met: _____

_____

Best story told: _____

_____

The kids liked this: _____

The best food: _____

_____

Games played: _____

_____

Something disappointing: _____

_____

Next time I'll do this differently: _____

_____

Henderson Beach State Park

City: Destin   County: Okaloosa

Plan your trip https://www.floridastateparks.org/index.php/parks-and-trails/henderson-beach-state-park

Activities:

- ❏ Beach Access
- ❏ Biking Trails
- ❏ Boating
- ❏ Campfire
- ❏ Caving
- ❏ Disc Golf
- ❏ Fishing
- ❏ Geo Cache
- ❏ Golf
- ❏ Hiking
- ❏ Horseback

- ❏ Hunting
- ❏ OHV
- ❏ Park Tours
- ❏ Rock Climbing
- ❏ Snorkeling
- ❏ Stargazing
- ❏ Swimming
- ❏ Viewpoint
- ❏ Wildlife & Birding
- ❏
- ❏

Facilities:

- ❏ ADA
- ❏ Gym
- ❏ Historic Sites
- ❏ Lodge
- ❏ Meeting Hall
- ❏ Pavilions
- ❏ Picnic sites
- ❏ Pool
- ❏ Restrooms

- ❏ Showers
- ❏ Visitor Center
- ❏ RV Camp
- ❏ Tent Camp
- ❏ Cabins
- ❏ Lodge Rooms
- ❏
- ❏
- ❏

Notes:

Get the Facts

- ❏ Phone: 850-837-7550
- ❏ Park Hours

  _____

- ❏ Reservations? ____Y ____N

  date made_____

- ❏ Open year 'round ___Y___N

  dates_____

- ❏ Check in time _____
- ❏ Check out time _____
- ❏ Dog friendly _____Y _____N
- ❏ Max RV length _____
- ❏ Distance from home

  miles: _____

  hours: _____

- ❏ Address_____

  _____

  _____

Fees:

- ❏ Day Use $ _____
- ❏ Camp Sites $_____
- ❏ RV Sites $ _____
- ❏ Refund policy

  _____

  _____

  _____

Make It Personal

Trip dates: _____

Why I went: _____

I went with: _____

How I got there: (circle all that apply) Plane   Train   Car   Bus   Bike   Hike   RV   MC

We stayed in (space, cabin, etc.) _____

The weather was: Sunny   Cloudy   Rainy   Stormy   Snowy   Foggy   Warm   Cold

Most relaxing day: _____

Something funny: _____

Someone we met: _____

Best story told: _____

The kids liked this: _____

The best food: _____

Games played: _____

Something disappointing: _____

Next time I'll do this differently: _____

Fred Gannon Rocky Bayou SP
City: Niceville   County: Okaloosa

Plan your trip https://www.floridastateparks.org/index.php/parks-and-trails/fred-gannon-rocky-bayou-state-park

Activities:

- ❑ Beach Access
- ❑ Biking Trails
- ❑ Boating
- ❑ Campfire
- ❑ Caving
- ❑ Disc Golf
- ❑ Fishing
- ❑ Geo Cache
- ❑ Golf
- ❑ Hiking
- ❑ Horseback

- ❑ Hunting
- ❑ OHV
- ❑ Park Tours
- ❑ Rock Climbing
- ❑ Snorkeling
- ❑ Stargazing
- ❑ Swimming
- ❑ Viewpoint
- ❑ Wildlife & Birding
- ❑
- ❑

Facilities:

- ❑ ADA
- ❑ Gym
- ❑ Historic Sites
- ❑ Lodge
- ❑ Meeting Hall
- ❑ Pavilions
- ❑ Picnic sites
- ❑ Pool
- ❑ Restrooms

- ❑ Showers
- ❑ Visitor Center
- ❑ RV Camp
- ❑ Tent Camp
- ❑ Cabins
- ❑ Lodge Rooms
- ❑
- ❑
- ❑

Notes:

Get the Facts

- ❑ Phone: 850-833-9144
- ❑ Park Hours

  _____

- ❑ Reservations? ____Y ____N

  date made_____

- ❑ Open year 'round ___Y___N

  dates_____

- ❑ Check in time _____

- ❑ Check out time _____

- ❑ Dog friendly _____Y _____N

- ❑ Max RV length _____

- ❑ Distance from home

  miles: _____

  hours: _____

- ❑ Address_____

  _____

  _____

Fees:

- ❑ Day Use $ _____
- ❑ Camp Sites $_____
- ❑ RV Sites $ _____
- ❑ Refund policy

  _____

  _____

  _____

Make It Personal

Trip dates:

Why I went:

I went with:

How I got there: (circle all that apply) Plane   Train   Car   Bus   Bike   Hike   RV   MC

We stayed in (space, cabin, etc.)

The weather was: Sunny   Cloudy   Rainy   Stormy   Snowy   Foggy   Warm   Cold

Most relaxing day:

Something funny:

Someone we met:

Best story told:

The kids liked this:

The best food:

Games played:

Something disappointing:

Next time I'll do this differently:

Blackwater River State Park
City: Milton   County: Santa Rosa

Plan your trip https://www.floridastateparks.org/parks-and-trails/blackwater-heritage-state-trail

Activities:

- ❑ Beach Access
- ❑ Biking Trails
- ❑ Boating
- ❑ Campfire
- ❑ Caving
- ❑ Disc Golf
- ❑ Fishing
- ❑ Geo Cache
- ❑ Golf
- ❑ Hiking
- ❑ Horseback

- ❑ Hunting
- ❑ OHV
- ❑ Park Tours
- ❑ Rock Climbing
- ❑ Snorkeling
- ❑ Stargazing
- ❑ Swimming
- ❑ Viewpoint
- ❑ Wildlife & Birding
- ❑
- ❑

Facilities:

- ❑ ADA
- ❑ Gym
- ❑ Historic Sites
- ❑ Lodge
- ❑ Meeting Hall
- ❑ Pavilions
- ❑ Picnic sites
- ❑ Pool
- ❑ Restrooms

- ❑ Showers
- ❑ Visitor Center
- ❑ RV Camp
- ❑ Tent Camp
- ❑ Cabins
- ❑ Lodge Rooms
- ❑
- ❑
- ❑

Notes:

Get the Facts

- ❑ Phone: 850-983-5338
- ❑ Park Hours

  _____

- ❑ Reservations? ____Y ____N

  date made_____

- ❑ Open year 'round ___Y___N

  dates_____

- ❑ Check in time _____
- ❑ Check out time _____
- ❑ Dog friendly _____Y _____N
- ❑ Max RV length _____
- ❑ Distance from home

  miles: _____

  hours: _____

- ❑ Address_____

  _____

  _____

Fees:

- ❑ Day Use $ _____
- ❑ Camp Sites $_____
- ❑ RV Sites $ _____
- ❑ Refund policy

  _____

  _____

  _____

Make It Personal

Trip dates: _____

Why I went: _____

I went with: _____

How I got there: (circle all that apply) Plane   Train   Car   Bus   Bike   Hike   RV   MC

We stayed in (space, cabin, etc.) _____

The weather was: Sunny   Cloudy   Rainy   Stormy   Snowy   Foggy   Warm   Cold

Most relaxing day: _____
_____

Something funny: _____
_____

Someone we met: _____
_____

Best story told: _____
_____

The kids liked this: _____

The best food: _____
_____

Games played: _____
_____

Something disappointing: _____
_____

Next time I'll do this differently: _____
_____

Grayton Beach State Park
City: Santa Rosa Beach   County: Walton

Plan your trip https://www.floridastateparks.org/index.php/graytonbeach

Activities:

- ❑ Beach Access
- ❑ Biking Trails
- ❑ Boating
- ❑ Campfire
- ❑ Caving
- ❑ Disc Golf
- ❑ Fishing
- ❑ Geo Cache
- ❑ Golf
- ❑ Hiking
- ❑ Horseback

- ❑ Hunting
- ❑ OHV
- ❑ Park Tours
- ❑ Rock Climbing
- ❑ Snorkeling
- ❑ Stargazing
- ❑ Swimming
- ❑ Viewpoint
- ❑ Wildlife & Birding
- ❑
- ❑

Facilities:

- ❑ ADA
- ❑ Gym
- ❑ Historic Sites
- ❑ Lodge
- ❑ Meeting Hall
- ❑ Pavilions
- ❑ Picnic sites
- ❑ Pool
- ❑ Restrooms

- ❑ Showers
- ❑ Visitor Center
- ❑ RV Camp
- ❑ Tent Camp
- ❑ Cabins
- ❑ Lodge Rooms
- ❑
- ❑
- ❑

Notes:

Get the Facts

- ❑ Phone: 850-267-8300
- ❑ Park Hours

  _____

- ❑ Reservations? ____Y ____N

  date made_____

- ❑ Open year 'round ___Y___N

  dates_____

- ❑ Check in time _____
- ❑ Check out time _____
- ❑ Dog friendly _____Y _____N
- ❑ Max RV length _____
- ❑ Distance from home

  miles: _____

  hours: _____

- ❑ Address_____

  _____

  _____

Fees:

- ❑ Day Use $ _____
- ❑ Camp Sites $_____
- ❑ RV Sites $ _____
- ❑ Refund policy

  _____

  _____

  _____

Make It Personal

Trip dates:

Why I went:

I went with:

How I got there: (circle all that apply) Plane   Train   Car   Bus   Bike   Hike   RV   MC

We stayed in (space, cabin, etc.)

The weather was: Sunny   Cloudy   Rainy   Stormy   Snowy   Foggy   Warm   Cold

Most relaxing day:

Something funny:

Someone we met:

Best story told:

The kids liked this:

The best food:

Games played:

Something disappointing:

Next time I'll do this differently:

Topsail Hill Preserve State Park
City: Santa Rosa Beach   County: Walton

Plan your trip https://www.floridastateparks.org/index.php/parks-and-trails/topsail-hill-preserve-state-park

Activities:

- ❏ Beach Access
- ❏ Biking Trails
- ❏ Boating
- ❏ Campfire
- ❏ Caving
- ❏ Disc Golf
- ❏ Fishing
- ❏ Geo Cache
- ❏ Golf
- ❏ Hiking
- ❏ Horseback

- ❏ Hunting
- ❏ OHV
- ❏ Park Tours
- ❏ Rock Climbing
- ❏ Snorkeling
- ❏ Stargazing
- ❏ Swimming
- ❏ Viewpoint
- ❏ Wildlife & Birding
- ❏
- ❏

Facilities:

- ❏ ADA
- ❏ Gym
- ❏ Historic Sites
- ❏ Lodge
- ❏ Meeting Hall
- ❏ Pavilions
- ❏ Picnic sites
- ❏ Pool
- ❏ Restrooms

- ❏ Showers
- ❏ Visitor Center
- ❏ RV Camp
- ❏ Tent Camp
- ❏ Cabins
- ❏ Lodge Rooms
- ❏
- ❏
- ❏

Notes:

Get the Facts

- ❏ Phone: 850-267-8330
- ❏ Park Hours

  _____

- ❏ Reservations? ____Y ____N

  date made_____

- ❏ Open year 'round ___Y___N

  dates_____

- ❏ Check in time _____
- ❏ Check out time _____
- ❏ Dog friendly _____Y _____N
- ❏ Max RV length _____
- ❏ Distance from home

  miles: _____

  hours: _____

- ❏ Address_____

  _____

  _____

Fees:

- ❏ Day Use $ _____
- ❏ Camp Sites $_____
- ❏ RV Sites $ _____
- ❏ Refund policy

  _____

  _____

  _____

Make It Personal

Trip dates: _____

Why I went: _____

I went with: _____

How I got there: (circle all that apply) Plane   Train   Car   Bus   Bike   Hike   RV   MC

We stayed in (space, cabin, etc.) _____

The weather was: Sunny   Cloudy   Rainy   Stormy   Snowy   Foggy   Warm   Cold

Most relaxing day: _____

Something funny: _____

Someone we met: _____

Best story told: _____

The kids liked this: _____

The best food: _____

Games played: _____

Something disappointing: _____

Next time I'll do this differently: _____

Falling Waters State Park
City: Chipley   County: Washington

Plan your trip https://www.floridastateparks.org/parks-and-trails/falling-waters-state-park

Activities:

- ❑ Beach Access
- ❑ Biking Trails
- ❑ Boating
- ❑ Campfire
- ❑ Caving
- ❑ Disc Golf
- ❑ Fishing
- ❑ Geo Cache
- ❑ Golf
- ❑ Hiking
- ❑ Horseback

- ❑ Hunting
- ❑ OHV
- ❑ Park Tours
- ❑ Rock Climbing
- ❑ Snorkeling
- ❑ Stargazing
- ❑ Swimming
- ❑ Viewpoint
- ❑ Wildlife & Birding
- ❑
- ❑

Facilities:

- ❑ ADA
- ❑ Gym
- ❑ Historic Sites
- ❑ Lodge
- ❑ Meeting Hall
- ❑ Pavilions
- ❑ Picnic sites
- ❑ Pool
- ❑ Restrooms

- ❑ Showers
- ❑ Visitor Center
- ❑ RV Camp
- ❑ Tent Camp
- ❑ Cabins
- ❑ Lodge Rooms
- ❑
- ❑
- ❑

Notes:

Get the Facts

- ❑ Phone: 850-638-6130
- ❑ Park Hours

    _____

- ❑ Reservations? ____Y ____N

    date made_____

- ❑ Open year 'round ___Y___N

    dates_____

- ❑ Check in time _____
- ❑ Check out time _____
- ❑ Dog friendly _____Y _____N
- ❑ Max RV length _____
- ❑ Distance from home

    miles: _____

    hours: _____

- ❑ Address_____

    _____

    _____

Fees:

- ❑ Day Use $ _____
- ❑ Camp Sites $_____
- ❑ RV Sites $ _____
- ❑ Refund policy

    _____

    _____

    _____

Make It Personal

Trip dates: _____

Why I went: _____

I went with: _____

How I got there: (circle all that apply) Plane   Train   Car   Bus   Bike   Hike   RV   MC

We stayed in (space, cabin, etc.) _____
_____

The weather was: Sunny   Cloudy   Rainy   Stormy   Snowy   Foggy   Warm   Cold

Most relaxing day: _____
_____

Something funny: _____
_____

Someone we met: _____
_____

Best story told: _____
_____

The kids liked this: _____

The best food: _____

Games played: _____

Something disappointing: _____

Next time I'll do this differently: _____

Perdido Key State Park
City: Pensacola   County: Escambia

Plan your trip: https://www.floridastateparks.org/parks-and-trails/perdido-key-state-park

Activities:

- ❑ Birding / Wildlife
- ❑ Fishing
- ❑ Guided tours
- ❑ Geo cache
- ❑ Hiking
- ❑ Horseback
- ❑ Hunting
- ❑ Snorkeling
- ❑ Trails
- ❑ Water access

Facilities:

- ❑ ADA
- ❑ Meeting hall
- ❑ Pavilions
- ❑ Picnic sites
- ❑ Restrooms
- ❑ Visitor center
- ❑
- ❑
- ❑
- ❑

Get the Facts

- ❑ Phone 850-492-1595
- ❑ Park Hours

  _____

- ❑ Reservations? ____Y ____N

  date made_____

- ❑ Open year 'round ___Y___N

  dates_____

- ❑ Distance from home

  miles: _____

  hours: _____

- ❑ Address or GPS

  _____

  _____

Date visited:

I went with:
_____

My favorite things:
_____

_____

_____

Fees:

- ❑ Day Use $ _____
- ❑ Parking $_____
- ❑ Refund policy

  _____

  _____

Notes

Tarkiln Bayou Preserve State Park
City: Pensacola   County: Escambia

Plan your trip: https://www.floridastateparks.org/parks-and-trails/tarkiln-bayou-preserve-state-park

Activities:

- ❑ Birding / Wildlife
- ❑ Fishing
- ❑ Guided tours
- ❑ Geo cache
- ❑ Hiking
- ❑ Horseback
- ❑ Hunting
- ❑ Snorkeling
- ❑ Trails
- ❑ Water access

Facilities:

- ❑ ADA
- ❑ Meeting hall
- ❑ Pavilions
- ❑ Picnic sites
- ❑ Restrooms
- ❑ Visitor center
- ❑
- ❑
- ❑
- ❑

Get the Facts

- ❑ Phone 850-492-1595
- ❑ Park Hours

  _____

- ❑ Reservations? ____Y ____N

  date made_____

- ❑ Open year 'round ___Y___N

  dates_____

- ❑ Distance from home

  miles: _____

  hours: _____

- ❑ Address or GPS

  _____

  _____

Date visited:

I went with:

_____

My favorite things:

_____

_____

_____

Notes

Fees:

- ❑ Day Use $ _____
- ❑ Parking $_____
- ❑ Refund policy

  _____

  _____

John Gorrie Museum State Park
City: Apalachicola   County: Franklin

Plan your trip: https://www.floridastateparks.org/index.php/parks-and-trails/john-gorrie-museum-state-park

Activities:

- ❑ Birding / Wildlife
- ❑ Fishing
- ❑ Guided tours
- ❑ Geo cache
- ❑ Hiking
- ❑ Horseback
- ❑ Hunting
- ❑ Snorkeling
- ❑ Trails
- ❑ Water access

Facilities:

- ❑ ADA
- ❑ Meeting hall
- ❑ Pavilions
- ❑ Picnic sites
- ❑ Restrooms
- ❑ Visitor center
- ❑
- ❑
- ❑
- ❑

Get the Facts

- ❑ Phone 850-653-9347
- ❑ Park Hours

  _____

- ❑ Reservations? ____Y ____N

  date made_____

- ❑ Open year 'round ___Y___N

  dates_____

- ❑ Distance from home

  miles: _____

  hours: _____

- ❑ Address or GPS

  _____

  _____

Date visited:

I went with:
_____

My favorite things:
_____

_____

_____

Notes

Fees:

- ❑ Day Use $ _____
- ❑ Parking $_____
- ❑ Refund policy

  _____

  _____

Orman House State Park
City: Apalachicola   County: Franklin

Plan your trip: https://www.floridastateparks.org/index.php/parks-and-trails/orman-house-historic-state-park

Activities:

- ❑ Birding / Wildlife
- ❑ Fishing
- ❑ Guided tours
- ❑ Geo cache
- ❑ Hiking
- ❑ Horseback
- ❑ Hunting
- ❑ Snorkeling
- ❑ Trails
- ❑ Water access

Facilities:

- ❑ ADA
- ❑ Meeting hall
- ❑ Pavilions
- ❑ Picnic sites
- ❑ Restrooms
- ❑ Visitor center
- ❑
- ❑
- ❑
- ❑

Get the Facts

- ❑ Phone 386-758-0400
- ❑ Park Hours

  _____

- ❑ Reservations? ____Y ____N

  date made_____

- ❑ Open year 'round ___Y___N

  dates_____

- ❑ Distance from home

  miles: _____

  hours: _____

- ❑ Address or GPS

  _____

  _____

Date visited:

I went with:

_____

My favorite things:

_____

_____

_____

Notes

Fees:

- ❑ Day Use $ _____
- ❑ Parking $_____
- ❑ Refund policy

  _____

  _____

Constitution Convention Museum SP
City: Port St. Joe   County: Gulf

Plan your trip: https://www.floridastateparks.org/parks-and-trails/constitution-convention-museum-state-park

Activities:

- ❏ Birding / Wildlife
- ❏ Fishing
- ❏ Guided tours
- ❏ Geo cache
- ❏ Hiking
- ❏ Horseback
- ❏ Hunting
- ❏ Snorkeling
- ❏ Trails
- ❏ Water access

Facilities:

- ❏ ADA
- ❏ Meeting hall
- ❏ Pavilions
- ❏ Picnic sites
- ❏ Restrooms
- ❏ Visitor center
- ❏
- ❏
- ❏
- ❏

Get the Facts

- ❏ Phone 850-229-8029
- ❏ Park Hours

    _____

- ❏ Reservations? ____ Y ____ N

    date made_____

- ❏ Open year 'round ___ Y ___ N

    dates_____

- ❏ Distance from home

    miles: _____

    hours: _____

- ❏ Address or GPS

    _____

    _____

Date visited:

I went with:
_____

My favorite things:
_____
_____
_____

Notes

Fees:

- ❏ Day Use $ _____
- ❏ Parking $_____
- ❏ Refund policy

    _____

    _____

Ponce de Leon Springs State Park
City: Ponce de Leon Springs County: Holmes

Plan your trip: https://www.floridastateparks.org/parks-and-trails/ponce-de-leon-springs-state-park

Activities:

- ❑ Birding / Wildlife
- ❑ Fishing
- ❑ Guided tours
- ❑ Geo cache
- ❑ Hiking
- ❑ Horseback
- ❑ Hunting
- ❑ Snorkeling
- ❑ Trails
- ❑ Water access

Facilities:

- ❑ ADA
- ❑ Meeting hall
- ❑ Pavilions
- ❑ Picnic sites
- ❑ Restrooms
- ❑ Visitor center
- ❑
- ❑
- ❑
- ❑

Get the Facts

- ❑ Phone 850-836-4281
- ❑ Park Hours

  _____

- ❑ Reservations? ____Y ____N

  date made_____

- ❑ Open year 'round ___Y___N

  dates_____

- ❑ Distance from home

  miles: _____

  hours: _____

- ❑ Address or GPS

  _____

  _____

Date visited:

I went with:

_____

My favorite things:

_____

_____

_____

Fees:

- ❑ Day Use $ _____
- ❑ Parking $_____
- ❑ Refund policy

  _____

  _____

Notes

Yellow River Marsh Preserve SP

City: Milton   County: Santa Rosa

Plan your trip: https://www.floridastateparks.org/parks-and-trails/yellow-river-marsh-preserve-state-park

Activities:

- ❑ Birding / Wildlife
- ❑ Fishing
- ❑ Guided tours
- ❑ Geo cache
- ❑ Hiking
- ❑ Horseback
- ❑ Hunting
- ❑ Snorkeling
- ❑ Trails
- ❑ Water access

Facilities:

- ❑ ADA
- ❑ Meeting hall
- ❑ Pavilions
- ❑ Picnic sites
- ❑ Restrooms
- ❑ Visitor center
- ❑
- ❑
- ❑
- ❑

Get the Facts

- ❑ Phone 850-983-5363
- ❑ Park Hours

  _____

- ❑ Reservations? ____Y ____N

  date made_____

- ❑ Open year 'round ___Y___N

  dates_____

- ❑ Distance from home

  miles: _____

  hours: _____

- ❑ Address or GPS

  _____

  _____

Date visited:

I went with:
_____

My favorite things:
_____

_____

_____

Notes

Fees:

- ❑ Day Use $ _____
- ❑ Parking $_____
- ❑ Refund policy

  _____

  _____

Deer Lake State Park
City: Santa Rosa   County: Walton

Plan your trip: https://www.floridastateparks.org/parks-and-trails/deer-lake-state-park

Activities:

- ❑ Birding / Wildlife
- ❑ Fishing
- ❑ Guided tours
- ❑ Geo cache
- ❑ Hiking
- ❑ Horseback
- ❑ Hunting
- ❑ Snorkeling
- ❑ Trails
- ❑ Water access

Facilities:

- ❑ ADA
- ❑ Meeting hall
- ❑ Pavilions
- ❑ Picnic sites
- ❑ Restrooms
- ❑ Visitor center
- ❑
- ❑
- ❑
- ❑

Get the Facts

- ❑ Phone 850-267-8300
- ❑ Park Hours

  _____

- ❑ Reservations? ____Y ____N

  date made_____

- ❑ Open year 'round ___Y___N

  dates_____

- ❑ Distance from home

  miles: _____

  hours: _____

- ❑ Address or GPS

  _____

  _____

Date visited:

I went with:
_____

My favorite things:
_____
_____
_____
_____

Notes

Fees:

- ❑ Day Use $ _____
- ❑ Parking $_____
- ❑ Refund policy

  _____
  _____

Eden Gardens State Park
City: Santa Rosa Beach   County: Walton

Plan your trip: https://www.floridastateparks.org/parks-and-trails/eden-gardens-state-park

Activities:

- ❑ Birding / Wildlife
- ❑ Fishing
- ❑ Guided tours
- ❑ Geo cache
- ❑ Hiking
- ❑ Horseback
- ❑ Hunting
- ❑ Snorkeling
- ❑ Trails
- ❑ Water access

Facilities:

- ❑ ADA
- ❑ Meeting hall
- ❑ Pavilions
- ❑ Picnic sites
- ❑ Restrooms
- ❑ Visitor center
- ❑
- ❑
- ❑
- ❑

Get the Facts

- ❑ Phone 850-267-8320
- ❑ Park Hours

  _____

- ❑ Reservations? ____Y ____N

  date made_____

- ❑ Open year 'round ___Y___N

  dates_____

- ❑ Distance from home

  miles: _____

  hours: _____

- ❑ Address or GPS

  _____

  _____

Date visited:

I went with:
_____

My favorite things:
_____

_____

_____

Fees:

- ❑ Day Use $ _____
- ❑ Parking $_____
- ❑ Refund policy

  _____

  _____

Notes

North Central

- Alachua
- Columbia
- Gilchrist
- Hamilton
- Jefferson
- Lafayette
- Leon
- Levy
- Madison
- Suwannee
- Taylor
- Wakulla

O'Leno State Park

City: High Springs   **County: Alachua**

Plan your Trip https://www.floridastateparks.org/parks-and-trails/oleno-state-park

Activities:

- ❑ Beach Access
- ❑ Biking Trails
- ❑ Boating
- ❑ Campfire
- ❑ Caving
- ❑ Disc Golf
- ❑ Fishing
- ❑ Geo Cache
- ❑ Golf
- ❑ Hiking
- ❑ Horseback

- ❑ Hunting
- ❑ OHV
- ❑ Park Tours
- ❑ Rock Climbing
- ❑ Snorkeling
- ❑ Stargazing
- ❑ Swimming
- ❑ Viewpoint
- ❑ Wildlife & Birding
- ❑
- ❑

Facilities:

- ❑ ADA
- ❑ Gym
- ❑ Historic Sites
- ❑ Lodge
- ❑ Meeting Hall
- ❑ Pavilions
- ❑ Picnic sites
- ❑ Pool
- ❑ Restrooms

- ❑ Showers
- ❑ Visitor Center
- ❑ RV Camp
- ❑ Tent Camp
- ❑ Cabins
- ❑ Lodge Rooms
- ❑
- ❑
- ❑

Notes:

Get the Facts

- ❑ Phone: 386-454-1853
- ❑ Park Hours

_____

- ❑ Reservations? ____Y ____N

date made_____

- ❑ Open year 'round ___Y___N

dates_____

- ❑ Check in time _____
- ❑ Check out time _____
- ❑ Dog friendly _____Y _____N
- ❑ Max RV length _____
- ❑ Distance from home

miles: _____

hours: _____

- ❑ Address_____

_____

_____

Fees:

- ❑ Day Use $ _____
- ❑ Camp Sites $_____
- ❑ RV Sites $ _____
- ❑ Refund policy

_____

_____

_____

Make It Personal

Trip dates: _____

Why I went: _____

I went with: _____

How I got there: (circle all that apply) Plane   Train   Car   Bus   Bike   Hike   RV   MC

We stayed in (space, cabin, etc.) _____

_____

The weather was: Sunny   Cloudy   Rainy   Stormy   Snowy   Foggy   Warm   Cold

Most relaxing day: _____

_____

Something funny: _____

_____

Someone we met: _____

_____

Best story told: _____

_____

The kids liked this: _____

The best food: _____

Games played: _____

_____

Something disappointing: _____

_____

Next time I'll do this differently: _____

_____

49

Ruth B. Kirby Gilchrist Blue Springs State Park

City: High Springs   County: Alachua

Plan your Trip https://www.floridastateparks.org/index.php/parks-and-trails/ruth-b-kirby-gilchrist-blue-springs-state-park

Activities:

- ❏ Beach Access
- ❏ Biking Trails
- ❏ Boating
- ❏ Campfire
- ❏ Caving
- ❏ Disc Golf
- ❏ Fishing
- ❏ Geo Cache
- ❏ Golf
- ❏ Hiking
- ❏ Horseback

- ❏ Hunting
- ❏ OHV
- ❏ Park Tours
- ❏ Rock Climbing
- ❏ Snorkeling
- ❏ Stargazing
- ❏ Swimming
- ❏ Viewpoint
- ❏ Wildlife & Birding
- ❏
- ❏

Facilities:

- ❏ ADA
- ❏ Gym
- ❏ Historic Sites
- ❏ Lodge
- ❏ Meeting Hall
- ❏ Pavilions
- ❏ Picnic sites
- ❏ Pool
- ❏ Restrooms

- ❏ Showers
- ❏ Visitor Center
- ❏ RV Camp
- ❏ Tent Camp
- ❏ Cabins
- ❏ Lodge Rooms
- ❏
- ❏
- ❏

Notes:

Get the Facts

- ❏ Phone: 386-454-1369
- ❏ Park Hours

  _____

- ❏ Reservations? ____Y ____N

  date made_____

- ❏ Open year 'round ___Y___N

  dates_____

- ❏ Check in time _____
- ❏ Check out time _____
- ❏ Dog friendly _____Y _____N
- ❏ Max RV length _____
- ❏ Distance from home

  miles: _____

  hours: _____

- ❏ Address_____

  _____

  _____

Fees:

- ❏ Day Use $ _____
- ❏ Camp Sites $_____
- ❏ RV Sites $ _____
- ❏ Refund policy

  _____

  _____

  _____

Make It Personal

Trip dates: _____

Why I went: _____

I went with: _____

How I got there: (circle all that apply) Plane   Train   Car   Bus   Bike   Hike   RV   MC

We stayed in (space, cabin, etc.)

_____

The weather was: Sunny Cloudy Rainy Stormy Snowy Foggy Warm Cold

Most relaxing day: _____

_____

Something funny: _____

_____

Someone we met: _____

_____

Best story told: _____

_____

The kids liked this: _____

The best food: _____

_____

Games played: _____

_____

Something disappointing: _____

_____

Next time I'll do this differently: _____

51

Paynes Prairie Preserve State Park

City: Micanopy   County: Alachua

Plan your Trip https://www.floridastateparks.org/parks-and-trails/paynes-prairie-preserve-state-park

Activities:

- ❑ Beach Access
- ❑ Biking Trails
- ❑ Boating
- ❑ Campfire
- ❑ Caving
- ❑ Disc Golf
- ❑ Fishing
- ❑ Geo Cache
- ❑ Golf
- ❑ Hiking
- ❑ Horseback

- ❑ Hunting
- ❑ OHV
- ❑ Park Tours
- ❑ Rock Climbing
- ❑ Snorkeling
- ❑ Stargazing
- ❑ Swimming
- ❑ Viewpoint
- ❑ Wildlife & Birding
- ❑
- ❑

Facilities:

- ❑ ADA
- ❑ Gym
- ❑ Historic Sites
- ❑ Lodge
- ❑ Meeting Hall
- ❑ Pavilions
- ❑ Picnic sites
- ❑ Pool
- ❑ Restrooms

- ❑ Showers
- ❑ Visitor Center
- ❑ RV Camp
- ❑ Tent Camp
- ❑ Cabins
- ❑ Lodge Rooms
- ❑
- ❑
- ❑

Notes:

Get the Facts

- ❑ Phone: 352-545-6000
- ❑ Park Hours

  _____

- ❑ Reservations? ____Y ____N

  date made_____

- ❑ Open year 'round ___Y___N

  dates_____

- ❑ Check in time _____
- ❑ Check out time _____
- ❑ Dog friendly _____Y _____N
- ❑ Max RV length _____
- ❑ Distance from home

  miles: _____

  hours: _____

- ❑ Address_____

  _____

  _____

Fees:

- ❑ Day Use $ _____
- ❑ Camp Sites $_____
- ❑ RV Sites $ _____
- ❑ Refund policy

  _____
  _____
  _____

52

Make It Personal

Trip dates:

Why I went:

I went with:

How I got there: (circle all that apply) Plane   Train   Car   Bus   Bike   Hike   RV   MC

We stayed in (space, cabin, etc.)

The weather was: Sunny   Cloudy   Rainy   Stormy   Snowy   Foggy   Warm   Cold

Most relaxing day:

Something funny:

Someone we met:

Best story told:

The kids liked this:

The best food:

Games played:

Something disappointing:

Next time I'll do this differently:

River Rise Preserve State Park
City: Fort White   County: Columbia

Plan your Trip https://www.floridastateparks.org/RiverRise

Activities:

- ❑ Beach Access
- ❑ Biking Trails
- ❑ Boating
- ❑ Campfire
- ❑ Caving
- ❑ Disc Golf
- ❑ Fishing
- ❑ Geo Cache
- ❑ Golf
- ❑ Hiking
- ❑ Horseback
- ❑ Hunting
- ❑ OHV
- ❑ Park Tours
- ❑ Rock Climbing
- ❑ Snorkeling
- ❑ Stargazing
- ❑ Swimming
- ❑ Viewpoint
- ❑ Wildlife & Birding
- ❑
- ❑

Facilities:

- ❑ ADA
- ❑ Gym
- ❑ Historic Sites
- ❑ Lodge
- ❑ Meeting Hall
- ❑ Pavilions
- ❑ Picnic sites
- ❑ Pool
- ❑ Restrooms
- ❑ Showers
- ❑ Visitor Center
- ❑ RV Camp
- ❑ Tent Camp
- ❑ Cabins
- ❑ Lodge Rooms
- ❑
- ❑
- ❑

Notes:

Get the Facts

- ❑ Phone: 386-454-1853
- ❑ Park Hours

    _____

- ❑ Reservations? ____Y ____N

    date made_____

- ❑ Open year 'round ___Y___N

    dates_____

- ❑ Check in time _____
- ❑ Check out time _____
- ❑ Dog friendly _____Y _____N
- ❑ Max RV length _____
- ❑ Distance from home

    miles: _____

    hours: _____

- ❑ Address_____

    _____

    _____

Fees:

- ❑ Day Use $ _____
- ❑ Camp Sites $_____
- ❑ RV Sites $ _____
- ❑ Refund policy

    _____

    _____

    _____

Make It Personal

Trip dates: _____

Why I went: _____

I went with: _____

How I got there: (circle all that apply) Plane   Train   Car   Bus   Bike   Hike   RV   MC

We stayed in (space, cabin, etc.) _____

_____

The weather was: Sunny   Cloudy   Rainy   Stormy   Snowy   Foggy   Warm   Cold

Most relaxing day: _____

_____

Something funny: _____

_____

Someone we met: _____

_____

Best story told: _____

_____

The kids liked this: _____

The best food: _____

_____

Games played: _____

_____

Something disappointing: _____

_____

Next time I'll do this differently: _____

_____

Fanning Springs State Park
City: Fanning Springs   County: Gilchrist / Levy

Plan your Trip https://www.floridastateparks.org/parks-and-trails/fanning-springs-state-park

Activities:

- ❑ Beach Access
- ❑ Biking Trails
- ❑ Boating
- ❑ Campfire
- ❑ Caving
- ❑ Disc Golf
- ❑ Fishing
- ❑ Geo Cache
- ❑ Golf
- ❑ Hiking
- ❑ Horseback

- ❑ Hunting
- ❑ OHV
- ❑ Park Tours
- ❑ Rock Climbing
- ❑ Snorkeling
- ❑ Stargazing
- ❑ Swimming
- ❑ Viewpoint
- ❑ Wildlife & Birding
- ❑
- ❑

Facilities:

- ❑ ADA
- ❑ Gym
- ❑ Historic Sites
- ❑ Lodge
- ❑ Meeting Hall
- ❑ Pavilions
- ❑ Picnic sites
- ❑ Pool
- ❑ Restrooms

- ❑ Showers
- ❑ Visitor Center
- ❑ RV Camp
- ❑ Tent Camp
- ❑ Cabins
- ❑ Lodge Rooms
- ❑
- ❑
- ❑

Notes:

Get the Facts

- ❑ Phone: 352-463-3420
- ❑ Park Hours

_____

- ❑ Reservations? ____Y ____N

date made_____

- ❑ Open year 'round ___Y___N

dates_____

- ❑ Check in time _____
- ❑ Check out time _____
- ❑ Dog friendly _____Y _____N
- ❑ Max RV length _____
- ❑ Distance from home

miles: _____

hours: _____

- ❑ Address_____

_____

_____

Fees:

- ❑ Day Use $ _____
- ❑ Camp Sites $_____
- ❑ RV Sites $ _____
- ❑ Refund policy

_____

_____

_____

Make It Personal

Trip dates: _____

Why I went: _____

I went with: _____

How I got there: (circle all that apply) Plane   Train   Car   Bus   Bike   Hike   RV   MC

We stayed in (space, cabin, etc.) _____

The weather was: Sunny   Cloudy   Rainy   Stormy   Snowy   Foggy   Warm   Cold

Most relaxing day: _____

Something funny: _____

Someone we met: _____

Best story told: _____

The kids liked this: _____

The best food: _____

Games played: _____

Something disappointing: _____

Next time I'll do this differently: _____

Stephen Foster Folk Cultural Center SP
City: White Springs   County: Hamilton

Plan your Trip https://www.floridastateparks.org/parks-and-trails/stephen-foster-folk-culture-center-state-park

Activities:

- ❑ Beach Access
- ❑ Biking Trails
- ❑ Boating
- ❑ Campfire
- ❑ Caving
- ❑ Disc Golf
- ❑ Fishing
- ❑ Geo Cache
- ❑ Golf
- ❑ Hiking
- ❑ Horseback

- ❑ Hunting
- ❑ OHV
- ❑ Park Tours
- ❑ Rock Climbing
- ❑ Snorkeling
- ❑ Stargazing
- ❑ Swimming
- ❑ Viewpoint
- ❑ Wildlife & Birding
- ❑
- ❑

Facilities:

- ❑ ADA
- ❑ Gym
- ❑ Historic Sites
- ❑ Lodge
- ❑ Meeting Hall
- ❑ Pavilions
- ❑ Picnic sites
- ❑ Pool
- ❑ Restrooms

- ❑ Showers
- ❑ Visitor Center
- ❑ RV Camp
- ❑ Tent Camp
- ❑ Cabins
- ❑ Lodge Rooms
- ❑
- ❑
- ❑

Notes:

Get the Facts

- ❑ Phone: 386-397-4331
- ❑ Park Hours

  _____

- ❑ Reservations? ____Y ____N

  date made_____

- ❑ Open year 'round ___Y___N

  dates_____

- ❑ Check in time _____
- ❑ Check out time _____
- ❑ Dog friendly _____Y _____N
- ❑ Max RV length _____
- ❑ Distance from home

  miles: _____

  hours: _____

- ❑ Address_____

  _____

  _____

Fees:

- ❑ Day Use $ _____
- ❑ Camp Sites $_____
- ❑ RV Sites $ _____
- ❑ Refund policy

  _____

  _____

  _____

58

Make It Personal

Trip dates:

Why I went:

I went with:

How I got there: (circle all that apply) Plane   Train   Car   Bus   Bike   Hike   RV   MC

We stayed in (space, cabin, etc.)

The weather was: Sunny   Cloudy   Rainy   Stormy   Snowy   Foggy   Warm   Cold

Most relaxing day:

Something funny:

Someone we met:

Best story told:

The kids liked this:

The best food:

Games played:

Something disappointing:

Next time I'll do this differently:

Lafayette Blue Springs State Park
City: Mayo   County: Lafayette

Plan your Trip https://www.floridastateparks.org/parks-and-trails/lafayette-blue-springs-state-park

Activities:

- ❑ Beach Access
- ❑ Biking Trails
- ❑ Boating
- ❑ Campfire
- ❑ Caving
- ❑ Disc Golf
- ❑ Fishing
- ❑ Geo Cache
- ❑ Golf
- ❑ Hiking
- ❑ Horseback

- ❑ Hunting
- ❑ OHV
- ❑ Park Tours
- ❑ Rock Climbing
- ❑ Snorkeling
- ❑ Stargazing
- ❑ Swimming
- ❑ Viewpoint
- ❑ Wildlife & Birding
- ❑
- ❑

Facilities:

- ❑ ADA
- ❑ Gym
- ❑ Historic Sites
- ❑ Lodge
- ❑ Meeting Hall
- ❑ Pavilions
- ❑ Picnic sites
- ❑ Pool
- ❑ Restrooms

- ❑ Showers
- ❑ Visitor Center
- ❑ RV Camp
- ❑ Tent Camp
- ❑ Cabins
- ❑ Lodge Rooms
- ❑
- ❑
- ❑

Notes:

Get the Facts

- ❑ Phone: 386-294-3667
- ❑ Park Hours

  _____

- ❑ Reservations? ____Y ____N

  date made_____

- ❑ Open year 'round ___Y___N

  dates_____

- ❑ Check in time _____
- ❑ Check out time _____
- ❑ Dog friendly _____Y _____N
- ❑ Max RV length _____
- ❑ Distance from home

  miles: _____

  hours: _____

- ❑ Address_____

  _____

  _____

Fees:

- ❑ Day Use $ _____
- ❑ Camp Sites $_____
- ❑ RV Sites $ _____
- ❑ Refund policy

  _____

  _____

  _____

Make It Personal

Trip dates: _____

Why I went: _____

I went with: _____

How I got there: (circle all that apply) Plane   Train   Car   Bus   Bike   Hike   RV   MC

We stayed in (space, cabin, etc.) _____

The weather was: Sunny Cloudy Rainy Stormy Snowy Foggy Warm Cold

Most relaxing day: _____

_____

Something funny: _____

_____

Someone we met: _____

_____

Best story told: _____

_____

The kids liked this: _____

The best food: _____

Games played: _____

Something disappointing: _____

Next time I'll do this differently: _____

Manatee Springs State Park
City: Chiefland   County: Levy

Plan your Trip https://www.floridastateparks.org/parks-and-trails/manatee-springs-state-park

Activities:

- ❑ Beach Access
- ❑ Biking Trails
- ❑ Boating
- ❑ Campfire
- ❑ Caving
- ❑ Disc Golf
- ❑ Fishing
- ❑ Geo Cache
- ❑ Golf
- ❑ Hiking
- ❑ Horseback

- ❑ Hunting
- ❑ OHV
- ❑ Park Tours
- ❑ Rock Climbing
- ❑ Snorkeling
- ❑ Stargazing
- ❑ Swimming
- ❑ Viewpoint
- ❑ Wildlife & Birding
- ❑
- ❑

Facilities:

- ❑ ADA
- ❑ Gym
- ❑ Historic Sites
- ❑ Lodge
- ❑ Meeting Hall
- ❑ Pavilions
- ❑ Picnic sites
- ❑ Pool
- ❑ Restrooms

- ❑ Showers
- ❑ Visitor Center
- ❑ RV Camp
- ❑ Tent Camp
- ❑ Cabins
- ❑ Lodge Rooms
- ❑
- ❑
- ❑

Notes:

Get the Facts

- ❑ Phone: 352-493-6072
- ❑ Park Hours

  _____

- ❑ Reservations? ____Y ____N

  date made_____

- ❑ Open year 'round ___Y___N

  dates_____

- ❑ Check in time _____
- ❑ Check out time _____
- ❑ Dog friendly ـ____Y ـ____N
- ❑ Max RV length _____
- ❑ Distance from home

  miles: _____

  hours: _____

- ❑ Address_____

  _____

  _____

Fees:

- ❑ Day Use $ _____
- ❑ Camp Sites $_____
- ❑ RV Sites $ _____
- ❑ Refund policy

  _____

  _____

  _____

Make It Personal

Trip dates: _____

Why I went: _____

I went with: _____

How I got there: (circle all that apply) Plane   Train   Car   Bus   Bike   Hike   RV   MC

We stayed in (space, cabin, etc.) _____

_____

The weather was: Sunny   Cloudy   Rainy   Stormy   Snowy   Foggy   Warm   Cold

Most relaxing day: _____

_____

Something funny: _____

_____

Someone we met: _____

_____

Best story told: _____

_____

The kids liked this: _____

The best food: _____

Games played: _____

_____

Something disappointing: _____

_____

Next time I'll do this differently: _____

_____

Waccasassa Bay Preserve State Park
City: Gulf Hammock   County: Levy

Plan your Trip https://www.floridastateparks.org/parks-and-trails/waccasassa-bay-preserve-state-park

Activities:

- ❑ Beach Access
- ❑ Biking Trails
- ❑ Boating
- ❑ Campfire
- ❑ Caving
- ❑ Disc Golf
- ❑ Fishing
- ❑ Geo Cache
- ❑ Golf
- ❑ Hiking
- ❑ Horseback

- ❑ Hunting
- ❑ OHV
- ❑ Park Tours
- ❑ Rock Climbing
- ❑ Snorkeling
- ❑ Stargazing
- ❑ Swimming
- ❑ Viewpoint
- ❑ Wildlife & Birding
- ❑
- ❑

Facilities:

- ❑ ADA
- ❑ Gym
- ❑ Historic Sites
- ❑ Lodge
- ❑ Meeting Hall
- ❑ Pavilions
- ❑ Picnic sites
- ❑ Pool
- ❑ Restrooms

- ❑ Showers
- ❑ Visitor Center
- ❑ RV Camp
- ❑ Tent Camp
- ❑ Cabins
- ❑ Lodge Rooms
- ❑
- ❑
- ❑

Notes:

Get the Facts

- ❑ Phone: 352-543-5567
- ❑ Park Hours

  _____

- ❑ Reservations? ____Y ____N

  date made_____

- ❑ Open year 'round ___Y___N

  dates_____

- ❑ Check in time _____
- ❑ Check out time _____
- ❑ Dog friendly _____Y _____N
- ❑ Max RV length _____
- ❑ Distance from home

  miles: _____

  hours: _____

- ❑ Address_____

  _____

  _____

Fees:

- ❑ Day Use $ _____
- ❑ Camp Sites $_____
- ❑ RV Sites $ _____
- ❑ Refund policy

  _____

  _____

  _____

Make It Personal

Trip dates:

Why I went:

I went with:

How I got there: (circle all that apply) Plane   Train   Car   Bus   Bike   Hike   RV   MC

We stayed in (space, cabin, etc.)

The weather was: Sunny   Cloudy   Rainy   Stormy   Snowy   Foggy   Warm   Cold

Most relaxing day:

Something funny:

Someone we met:

Best story told:

The kids liked this:

The best food:

Games played:

Something disappointing:

Next time I'll do this differently:

Suwannee River State Park
City: Live Oak   County: Suwannee

Plan your Trip https://www.floridastateparks.org/parks-and-trails/suwannee-river-state-park

Activities:

- ❑ Beach Access
- ❑ Biking Trails
- ❑ Boating
- ❑ Campfire
- ❑ Caving
- ❑ Disc Golf
- ❑ Fishing
- ❑ Geo Cache
- ❑ Golf
- ❑ Hiking
- ❑ Horseback

- ❑ Hunting
- ❑ OHV
- ❑ Park Tours
- ❑ Rock Climbing
- ❑ Snorkeling
- ❑ Stargazing
- ❑ Swimming
- ❑ Viewpoint
- ❑ Wildlife & Birding
- ❑
- ❑

Facilities:

- ❑ ADA
- ❑ Gym
- ❑ Historic Sites
- ❑ Lodge
- ❑ Meeting Hall
- ❑ Pavilions
- ❑ Picnic sites
- ❑ Pool
- ❑ Restrooms

- ❑ Showers
- ❑ Visitor Center
- ❑ RV Camp
- ❑ Tent Camp
- ❑ Cabins
- ❑ Lodge Rooms
- ❑
- ❑
- ❑

Notes:

Get the Facts

- ❑ Phone: 386-362-2746
- ❑ Park Hours

  _____

- ❑ Reservations? ____Y ____N

  date made_____

- ❑ Open year 'round ___Y___N

  dates_____

- ❑ Check in time _____

- ❑ Check out time _____

- ❑ Dog friendly _____Y _____N

- ❑ Max RV length _____

- ❑ Distance from home

  miles: _____

  hours: _____

- ❑ Address_____

  _____

  _____

Fees:

- ❑ Day Use $ _____
- ❑ Camp Sites $_____
- ❑ RV Sites $ _____
- ❑ Refund policy

  _____

  _____

  _____

Make It Personal

Trip dates:

Why I went:

I went with:

How I got there: (circle all that apply) Plane   Train   Car   Bus   Bike   Hike   RV   MC

We stayed in (space, cabin, etc.)

The weather was: Sunny   Cloudy   Rainy   Stormy   Snowy   Foggy   Warm   Cold

Most relaxing day:

Something funny:

Someone we met:

Best story told:

The kids liked this:

The best food:

Games played:

Something disappointing:

Next time I'll do this differently:

Ochlockonee River State Park
City: Sopchoppy   County: Wakulla

Plan your Trip https://www.floridastateparks.org/parks-and-trails/ochlockonee-river-state-park

Activities:

- ❑ Beach Access
- ❑ Biking Trails
- ❑ Boating
- ❑ Campfire
- ❑ Caving
- ❑ Disc Golf
- ❑ Fishing
- ❑ Geo Cache
- ❑ Golf
- ❑ Hiking
- ❑ Horseback

- ❑ Hunting
- ❑ OHV
- ❑ Park Tours
- ❑ Rock Climbing
- ❑ Snorkeling
- ❑ Stargazing
- ❑ Swimming
- ❑ Viewpoint
- ❑ Wildlife & Birding
- ❑
- ❑

Facilities:

- ❑ ADA
- ❑ Gym
- ❑ Historic Sites
- ❑ Lodge
- ❑ Meeting Hall
- ❑ Pavilions
- ❑ Picnic sites
- ❑ Pool
- ❑ Restrooms

- ❑ Showers
- ❑ Visitor Center
- ❑ RV Camp
- ❑ Tent Camp
- ❑ Cabins
- ❑ Lodge Rooms
- ❑
- ❑
- ❑

Notes:

Get the Facts

- ❑ Phone: 850-962-2771
- ❑ Park Hours

  _____

- ❑ Reservations? ____Y ____N

  date made_____

- ❑ Open year 'round ___Y___N

  dates_____

- ❑ Check in time _____
- ❑ Check out time _____
- ❑ Dog friendly _____Y _____N
- ❑ Max RV length _____
- ❑ Distance from home

  miles: _____

  hours: _____

- ❑ Address_____

  _____

  _____

Fees:

- ❑ Day Use $ _____
- ❑ Camp Sites $_____
- ❑ RV Sites $ _____
- ❑ Refund policy

  _____

  _____

  _____

Make It Personal

Trip dates:

Why I went:

I went with:

How I got there: (circle all that apply) Plane   Train   Car   Bus   Bike   Hike   RV   MC

We stayed in (space, cabin, etc.)

The weather was: Sunny   Cloudy   Rainy   Stormy   Snowy   Foggy   Warm   Cold

Most relaxing day:

Something funny:

Someone we met:

Best story told:

The kids liked this:

The best food:

Games played:

Something disappointing:

Next time I'll do this differently:

Edward Ball Wakulla Springs State Park

City: Wakulla Springs   County: Wakulla

Plan your Trip https://www.floridastateparks.org/WakullaSprings

Activities:

- ❑ Beach Access
- ❑ Biking Trails
- ❑ Boating
- ❑ Campfire
- ❑ Caving
- ❑ Disc Golf
- ❑ Fishing
- ❑ Geo Cache
- ❑ Golf
- ❑ Hiking
- ❑ Horseback

- ❑ Hunting
- ❑ OHV
- ❑ Park Tours
- ❑ Rock Climbing
- ❑ Snorkeling
- ❑ Stargazing
- ❑ Swimming
- ❑ Viewpoint
- ❑ Wildlife & Birding
- ❑
- ❑

Facilities:

- ❑ ADA
- ❑ Gym
- ❑ Historic Sites
- ❑ Lodge
- ❑ Meeting Hall
- ❑ Pavilions
- ❑ Picnic sites
- ❑ Pool
- ❑ Restrooms

- ❑ Showers
- ❑ Visitor Center
- ❑ RV Camp
- ❑ Tent Camp
- ❑ Cabins
- ❑ Lodge Rooms
- ❑
- ❑
- ❑

Notes:

Get the Facts

- ❑ Phone: 850-561-7276
- ❑ Park Hours

  _____

- ❑ Reservations? ____Y ____N

  date made_____

- ❑ Open year 'round ___Y___N

  dates_____

- ❑ Check in time _____
- ❑ Check out time _____
- ❑ Dog friendly _____Y _____N
- ❑ Max RV length _____
- ❑ Distance from home

  miles: _____

  hours: _____

- ❑ Address_____

  _____

  _____

Fees:

- ❑ Day Use $ _____
- ❑ Camp Sites $_____
- ❑ RV Sites $ _____
- ❑ Refund policy

  _____

  _____

  _____

Make It Personal

Trip dates:

Why I went:

I went with:

How I got there: (circle all that apply) Plane   Train   Car   Bus   Bike   Hike   RV   MC

We stayed in (space, cabin, etc.)

The weather was: Sunny   Cloudy   Rainy   Stormy   Snowy   Foggy   Warm   Cold

Most relaxing day:

Something funny:

Someone we met:

Best story told:

The kids liked this:

The best food:

Games played:

Something disappointing:

Next time I'll do this differently:

San Felasco Hammock Preserve SP
City: Alachua   County: Alachua

Plan your trip https://www.floridastateparks.org/parks-and-trails/san-felasco-hammock-preserve-state-park

Activities:

- ❑ Birding / Wildlife
- ❑ Fishing
- ❑ Guided tours
- ❑ Geo cache
- ❑ Hiking
- ❑ Horseback
- ❑ Hunting
- ❑ Snorkeling
- ❑ Trails
- ❑ Water access

Facilities:

- ❑ ADA
- ❑ Meeting hall
- ❑ Pavilions
- ❑ Picnic sites
- ❑ Restrooms
- ❑ Visitor center
- ❑
- ❑
- ❑
- ❑

Get the Facts

- ❑ Phone 386-462-7905
- ❑ Park Hours

  _____

- ❑ Reservations? ____Y ____N

  date made_____

- ❑ Open year 'round ___Y___N

  dates_____

- ❑ Distance from home

  miles: _____

  hours: _____

- ❑ Address or GPS

  _____

  _____

Date visited:

I went with:
_____

My favorite things:
_____

_____

_____

Fees:

- ❑ Day Use $ _____
- ❑ Parking $_____
- ❑ Refund policy

  _____

  _____

Notes

Marjorie Kinnan Rawlings Historic SP
City: Cross Creek   County: Alachua

Plan your trip https://www.floridastateparks.org/index.php/parks-and-trails/marjorie-kinnan-rawlings-historic-state-park

Activities:

- ❑ Birding / Wildlife
- ❑ Fishing
- ❑ Guided tours
- ❑ Geo cache
- ❑ Hiking
- ❑ Horseback
- ❑ Hunting
- ❑ Snorkeling
- ❑ Trails
- ❑ Water access

Facilities:

- ❑ ADA
- ❑ Meeting hall
- ❑ Pavilions
- ❑ Picnic sites
- ❑ Restrooms
- ❑ Visitor center
- ❑
- ❑
- ❑
- ❑

Get the Facts

- ❑ Phone 352-466-3672
- ❑ Park Hours

  _____

- ❑ Reservations? ____Y ____N

  date made_____

- ❑ Open year 'round ___Y___N

  dates_____

- ❑ Distance from home

  miles: _____

  hours: _____

- ❑ Address or GPS

  _____

  _____

Date visited:

I went with:

_____

My favorite things:

_____

_____

_____

Notes

Fees:

- ❑ Day Use $ _____
- ❑ Parking $_____
- ❑ Refund policy

  _____

  _____

Devils Milhopper Geological SP
City: Gainesville   County: Alachua

Plan your trip https://www.floridastateparks.org/parks-and-trails/devils-millhopper-geological-state-park

Activities:

- ❑ Birding / Wildlife
- ❑ Fishing
- ❑ Guided tours
- ❑ Geo cache
- ❑ Hiking
- ❑ Horseback
- ❑ Hunting
- ❑ Snorkeling
- ❑ Trails
- ❑ Water access

Facilities:

- ❑ ADA
- ❑ Meeting hall
- ❑ Pavilions
- ❑ Picnic sites
- ❑ Restrooms
- ❑ Visitor center
- ❑
- ❑
- ❑
- ❑

Get the Facts

- ❑ Phone 352-955-2008
- ❑ Park Hours

  _____

- ❑ Reservations? ____Y ____N

  date made_____

- ❑ Open year 'round ___Y___N

  dates_____

- ❑ Distance from home

  miles: _____

  hours: _____

- ❑ Address or GPS

  _____

  _____

Date visited:

I went with:

_____

My favorite things:

_____

_____

_____

Notes

Fees:

- ❑ Day Use $ _____
- ❑ Parking $_____
- ❑ Refund policy

  _____

  _____

Price's Scrub State Park
City: Micanopy   County: Alachua

Plan your trip https://www.floridastateparks.org/parks-and-trails/prices-scrub-state-park

Activities:

- ❏ Birding / Wildlife
- ❏ Fishing
- ❏ Guided tours
- ❏ Geo cache
- ❏ Hiking
- ❏ Horseback
- ❏ Hunting
- ❏ Snorkeling
- ❏ Trails
- ❏ Water access

Facilities:

- ❏ ADA
- ❏ Meeting hall
- ❏ Pavilions
- ❏ Picnic sites
- ❏ Restrooms
- ❏ Visitor center
- ❏
- ❏
- ❏
- ❏

Get the Facts

- ❏ Phone 352-466-3397
- ❏ Park Hours

  _____

- ❏ Reservations? ____Y ____N

  date made_____

- ❏ Open year 'round ___Y___N

  dates_____

- ❏ Distance from home

  miles: _____

  hours: _____

- ❏ Address or GPS

  _____

  _____

Date visited:

I went with:
_____

My favorite things:
_____

_____

_____

Fees:

- ❏ Day Use $ _____
- ❏ Parking $_____
- ❏ Refund policy

  _____

  _____

Notes

Dudley Farm Historic State Park
City: Newberry   County: Alachua

Plan your trip https://www.floridastateparks.org/parks-and-trails/dudley-farm-historic-state-park

Activities:

- ❑ Birding / Wildlife
- ❑ Fishing
- ❑ Guided tours
- ❑ Geo cache
- ❑ Hiking
- ❑ Horseback
- ❑ Hunting
- ❑ Snorkeling
- ❑ Trails
- ❑ Water access

Facilities:

- ❑ ADA
- ❑ Meeting hall
- ❑ Pavilions
- ❑ Picnic sites
- ❑ Restrooms
- ❑ Visitor center
- ❑
- ❑
- ❑
- ❑

Get the Facts

- ❑ Phone 352-472-1142
- ❑ Park Hours

  _____

- ❑ Reservations? ____Y ____N

  date made_____

- ❑ Open year 'round ___Y___N

  dates_____

- ❑ Distance from home

  miles: _____

  hours: _____

- ❑ Address or GPS

  _____

  _____

Date visited:

I went with:

_____

My favorite things:

_____

_____

_____

Notes

Fees:

- ❑ Day Use $ _____
- ❑ Parking $_____
- ❑ Refund policy

  _____

  _____

76

Ichetucknee Springs State Park
City: Fort White   County: Columbia

Plan your trip: https://www.floridastateparks.org/parks-and-trails/ichetucknee-springs-state-park

Activities:

- ❑ Birding / Wildlife
- ❑ Fishing
- ❑ Guided tours
- ❑ Geo cache
- ❑ Hiking
- ❑ Horseback
- ❑ Hunting
- ❑ Snorkeling
- ❑ Trails
- ❑ Water access

Facilities:

- ❑ ADA
- ❑ Meeting hall
- ❑ Pavilions
- ❑ Picnic sites
- ❑ Restrooms
- ❑ Visitor center
- ❑
- ❑
- ❑
- ❑

Get the Facts

- ❑ Phone 386-497-4690
- ❑ Park Hours

  _____

- ❑ Reservations? ____Y ____N

  date made_____

- ❑ Open year 'round ___Y___N

  dates_____

- ❑ Distance from home

  miles: _____

  hours: _____

- ❑ Address or GPS

  _____

  _____

Date visited:

I went with:

_____

My favorite things:

_____

_____

_____

Notes

Fees:

- ❑ Day Use $ _____
- ❑ Parking $_____
- ❑ Refund policy

  _____

  _____

Big Shoals State Park
City: White Springs   County: Hamilton

Plan your trip: https://www.floridastateparks.org/index.php/parks-and-trails/big-shoals-state-park

Activities:

- ❑ Birding / Wildlife
- ❑ Fishing
- ❑ Guided tours
- ❑ Geo cache
- ❑ Hiking
- ❑ Horseback
- ❑ Hunting
- ❑ Snorkeling
- ❑ Trails
- ❑ Water access

Facilities:

- ❑ ADA
- ❑ Meeting hall
- ❑ Pavilions
- ❑ Picnic sites
- ❑ Restrooms
- ❑ Visitor center
- ❑
- ❑
- ❑
- ❑

Get the Facts

- ❑ Phone 386-397-4331
- ❑ Park Hours

_____

- ❑ Reservations? ____Y ____N

date made_____

- ❑ Open year 'round ___Y___N

dates_____

- ❑ Distance from home

miles: _____

hours: _____

- ❑ Address or GPS

_____

_____

Date visited:

I went with:
_____

My favorite things:
_____

_____

_____

Fees:

- ❑ Day Use $ _____
- ❑ Parking $_____
- ❑ Refund policy

_____

_____

Notes

Econfina River State Park
City: Lamont   County: Jefferson

Plan your trip: https://www.floridastateparks.org/parks-and-trails/econfina-river-state-park

Activities:

- ❑ Birding / Wildlife
- ❑ Fishing
- ❑ Guided tours
- ❑ Geo cache
- ❑ Hiking
- ❑ Horseback
- ❑ Hunting
- ❑ Snorkeling
- ❑ Trails
- ❑ Water access

Facilities:

- ❑ ADA
- ❑ Meeting hall
- ❑ Pavilions
- ❑ Picnic sites
- ❑ Restrooms
- ❑ Visitor center
- ❑
- ❑
- ❑
- ❑

Get the Facts

- ❑ Phone 850-487-7989
- ❑ Park Hours

  _____

- ❑ Reservations? ____Y ____N

  date made_____

- ❑ Open year 'round ___Y___N

  dates_____

- ❑ Distance from home

  miles: _____

  hours: _____

- ❑ Address or GPS

  _____

  _____

Date visited:

I went with:
_____

My favorite things:
_____

_____

_____

Notes

Fees:

- ❑ Day Use $ _____
- ❑ Parking $_____
- ❑ Refund policy

  _____

  _____

Alfred B. Maclay Gardens State Park
City: Tallahassee   County: Leon

Plan your trip: https://www.floridastateparks.org/MaclayGardens

Activities:

- ❑ Birding / Wildlife
- ❑ Fishing
- ❑ Guided tours
- ❑ Geo cache
- ❑ Hiking
- ❑ Horseback
- ❑ Hunting
- ❑ Snorkeling
- ❑ Trails
- ❑ Water access

Facilities:

- ❑ ADA
- ❑ Meeting hall
- ❑ Pavilions
- ❑ Picnic sites
- ❑ Restrooms
- ❑ Visitor center
- ❑
- ❑
- ❑
- ❑

Get the Facts

- ❑ Phone 850-487-4556
- ❑ Park Hours

  _____

- ❑ Reservations? ____Y ____N

  date made_____

- ❑ Open year 'round ___Y___N

  dates_____

- ❑ Distance from home

  miles: _____

  hours: _____

- ❑ Address or GPS

  _____

  _____

Date visited:

I went with:
_____

My favorite things:
_____

_____

_____

Notes

Fees:

- ❑ Day Use $ _____
- ❑ Parking $_____
- ❑ Refund policy

  _____

  _____

Lake Jackson Mounds Archaeological SP
City: Tallahassee   County: Leon

Plan your trip: https://www.floridastateparks.org/index.php/parks-and-trails/lake-jackson-mounds-archaeological-state-park

Activities:

❏ Birding / Wildlife
❏ Fishing
❏ Guided tours
❏ Geo cache
❏ Hiking
❏ Horseback
❏ Hunting
❏ Snorkeling
❏ Trails
❏ Water access

Facilities:

❏ ADA
❏ Meeting hall
❏ Pavilions
❏ Picnic sites
❏ Restrooms
❏ Visitor center
❏
❏
❏
❏

Get the Facts

❏ Phone 850-487-7989
❏ Park Hours

_____

❏ Reservations? ____Y ____N

date made_____

❏ Open year 'round ___Y___N

dates_____

❏ Distance from home

miles: _____

hours: _____

❏ Address or GPS

_____

_____

Date visited:

I went with:
_____

My favorite things:
_____

_____

_____

Notes

Fees:

❏ Day Use $ _____
❏ Parking $_____
❏ Refund policy

_____

_____

Lake Talquin State Park
City: Tallahassee   County: Leon

Plan your trip: https://www.floridastateparks.org/index.php/parks-and-trails/lake-talquin-state-park

Activities:

- ❏ Birding / Wildlife
- ❏ Fishing
- ❏ Guided tours
- ❏ Geo cache
- ❏ Hiking
- ❏ Horseback
- ❏ Hunting
- ❏ Snorkeling
- ❏ Trails
- ❏ Water access

Facilities:

- ❏ ADA
- ❏ Meeting hall
- ❏ Pavilions
- ❏ Picnic sites
- ❏ Restrooms
- ❏ Visitor center
- ❏
- ❏
- ❏
- ❏

Get the Facts

- ❏ Phone 850-487-7989
- ❏ Park Hours

  _____

- ❏ Reservations? ____Y ____N

  date made_____

- ❏ Open year 'round ___Y___N

  dates_____

- ❏ Distance from home

  miles: _____

  hours: _____

- ❏ Address or GPS

  _____

  _____

Date visited:

I went with:

_____

My favorite things:

_____

_____

_____

Notes

Fees:

- ❏ Day Use $ _____
- ❏ Parking $_____
- ❏ Refund policy

  _____

  _____

Letchworth-Love Mounds Archaeological SP

City: Tallahassee   County: Leon

Plan your trip: https://www.floridastateparks.org/parks-and-trails/letchworth-love-mounds-archaeological-state-park

Activities:

- ❑ Birding / Wildlife
- ❑ Fishing
- ❑ Guided tours
- ❑ Geo cache
- ❑ Hiking
- ❑ Horseback
- ❑ Hunting
- ❑ Snorkeling
- ❑ Trails
- ❑ Water access

Facilities:

- ❑ ADA
- ❑ Meeting hall
- ❑ Pavilions
- ❑ Picnic sites
- ❑ Restrooms
- ❑ Visitor center
- ❑
- ❑
- ❑
- ❑

Get the Facts

- ❑ Phone 850-487-7989
- ❑ Park Hours

  _____

- ❑ Reservations? ____Y ____N

  date made_____

- ❑ Open year 'round ___Y___N

  dates_____

- ❑ Distance from home

  miles: _____

  hours: _____

- ❑ Address or GPS

  _____

  _____

Date visited:

I went with:

_____

My favorite things:

_____

_____

_____

Notes

Fees:

- ❑ Day Use $ _____
- ❑ Parking $_____
- ❑ Refund policy

  _____

  _____

Natural Bridge Battlefield Historic SP
City: Tallahassee   County: Leon

Plan your trip: https://www.floridastateparks.org/index.php/parks-and-trails/natural-bridge-battlefield-historic-state-park

Activities:

- ❑ Birding / Wildlife
- ❑ Fishing
- ❑ Guided tours
- ❑ Geo cache
- ❑ Hiking
- ❑ Horseback
- ❑ Hunting
- ❑ Snorkeling
- ❑ Trails
- ❑ Water access

Facilities:

- ❑ ADA
- ❑ Meeting hall
- ❑ Pavilions
- ❑ Picnic sites
- ❑ Restrooms
- ❑ Visitor center
- ❑
- ❑
- ❑
- ❑

Get the Facts

- ❑ Phone 850-487-7989
- ❑ Park Hours

   _____

- ❑ Reservations? ____Y ____N

   date made_____
- ❑ Open year 'round ___Y___N

   dates_____
- ❑ Distance from home

   miles: _____

   hours: _____
- ❑ Address or GPS

   _____

   _____

Date visited:

I went with:
_____

My favorite things:
_____

_____

_____

Notes

Fees:

- ❑ Day Use $ _____
- ❑ Parking $_____
- ❑ Refund policy

   _____

   _____

St. Marks River Preserve State Park
City: Tallahassee   County: Leon

Plan your trip: https://www.floridastateparks.org/parks-and-trails/st-marks-river-preserve-state-park

Activities:

- ❑ Birding / Wildlife
- ❑ Fishing
- ❑ Guided tours
- ❑ Geo cache
- ❑ Hiking
- ❑ Horseback
- ❑ Hunting
- ❑ Snorkeling
- ❑ Trails
- ❑ Water access

Facilities:

- ❑ ADA
- ❑ Meeting hall
- ❑ Pavilions
- ❑ Picnic sites
- ❑ Restrooms
- ❑ Visitor center
- ❑
- ❑
- ❑
- ❑

Get the Facts

- ❑ Phone 850-487-7989
- ❑ Park Hours

  _____

- ❑ Reservations? ____Y ____N

  date made_____

- ❑ Open year 'round ___Y___N

  dates_____

- ❑ Distance from home

  miles: _____

  hours: _____

- ❑ Address or GPS

  _____

  _____

Date visited:

I went with:

_____

My favorite things:

_____

_____

_____

Notes

Fees:

- ❑ Day Use $ _____
- ❑ Parking $_____
- ❑ Refund policy

  _____

  _____

Cedar Key Museum State Park
City: Cedar Key   County: Levy

Plan your trip https://www.floridastateparks.org/parks-and-trails/cedar-key-museum-state-park

Activities:

- ❑ Birding / Wildlife
- ❑ Fishing
- ❑ Guided tours
- ❑ Geo cache
- ❑ Hiking
- ❑ Horseback
- ❑ Hunting
- ❑ Snorkeling
- ❑ Trails
- ❑ Water access

Facilities:

- ❑ ADA
- ❑ Meeting hall
- ❑ Pavilions
- ❑ Picnic sites
- ❑ Restrooms
- ❑ Visitor center
- ❑
- ❑
- ❑
- ❑

Get the Facts

- ❑ Phone 352-543-5350
- ❑ Park Hours

  _____

- ❑ Reservations? ____Y ____N

  date made_____

- ❑ Open year 'round ___Y___N

  dates_____

- ❑ Distance from home

  miles: _____

  hours: _____

- ❑ Address or GPS

  _____

  _____

Date visited:

I went with:

_____

My favorite things:

_____

_____

_____

Fees:

- ❑ Day Use $ _____
- ❑ Parking $_____
- ❑ Refund policy

  _____

  _____

Notes

Cedar Key Scrub State Preserve
City: Cedar Key   County: Levy

Plan your trip https://www.floridastateparks.org/parks-and-trails/cedar-key-scrub-state-reserve

Activities:

- ❑ Birding / Wildlife
- ❑ Fishing
- ❑ Guided tours
- ❑ Geo cache
- ❑ Hiking
- ❑ Horseback
- ❑ Hunting
- ❑ Snorkeling
- ❑ Trails
- ❑ Water access

Facilities:

- ❑ ADA
- ❑ Meeting hall
- ❑ Pavilions
- ❑ Picnic sites
- ❑ Restrooms
- ❑ Visitor center
- ❑
- ❑
- ❑
- ❑

Get the Facts

- ❑ Phone 352-543-5567
- ❑ Park Hours

  _____

- ❑ Reservations? ____Y ____N

  date made_____

- ❑ Open year 'round ___Y___N

  dates_____

- ❑ Distance from home

  miles: _____

  hours: _____

- ❑ Address or GPS

  _____

  _____

Date visited:

I went with:
_____

My favorite things:
_____

_____

_____

Notes

Fees:

- ❑ Day Use $ _____
- ❑ Parking $_____
- ❑ Refund policy

  _____

  _____

Inglis Bypass Recreation Area
City: Inglis　　　　　　　County: Levy

Plan your trip https://www.floridastateparks.org/index.php/parks-and-trails/inglis-bypass-recreation-area

Activities:

- ❑ Birding / Wildlife
- ❑ Fishing
- ❑ Guided tours
- ❑ Geo cache
- ❑ Hiking
- ❑ Horseback
- ❑ Hunting
- ❑ Snorkeling
- ❑ Trails
- ❑ Water access

Facilities:

- ❑ ADA
- ❑ Meeting hall
- ❑ Pavilions
- ❑ Picnic sites
- ❑ Restrooms
- ❑ Visitor center
- ❑
- ❑
- ❑
- ❑

Get the Facts

- ❑ Phone 352-236-7143
- ❑ Park Hours

  _____

- ❑ Reservations? ____Y ____N

  date made_____

- ❑ Open year 'round ___Y___N

  dates_____

- ❑ Distance from home

  miles: _____

  hours: _____

- ❑ Address or GPS

  _____

  _____

Date visited:

I went with:
_____

My favorite things:
_____

_____

_____

Notes

Fees:

- ❑ Day Use $ _____
- ❑ Parking $_____
- ❑ Refund policy

  _____

  _____

Inglis Lock Recreation Area
City: Inglis   County: Levy

Plan your trip https://www.floridastateparks.org/parks-and-trails/inglis-lock-recreation-area

Activities:

- ❑ Birding / Wildlife
- ❑ Fishing
- ❑ Guided tours
- ❑ Geo cache
- ❑ Hiking
- ❑ Horseback
- ❑ Hunting
- ❑ Snorkeling
- ❑ Trails
- ❑ Water access

Facilities:

- ❑ ADA
- ❑ Meeting hall
- ❑ Pavilions
- ❑ Picnic sites
- ❑ Restrooms
- ❑ Visitor center
- ❑
- ❑
- ❑
- ❑

Get the Facts

- ❑ Phone 352-236-7143
- ❑ Park Hours

   _____

- ❑ Reservations? ____Y ____N

   date made_____

- ❑ Open year 'round ___Y___N

   dates_____

- ❑ Distance from home

   miles: _____

   hours: _____

- ❑ Address or GPS

   _____

   _____

Date visited:

I went with:
_____

My favorite things:
_____

_____

_____

Notes

Fees:

- ❑ Day Use $ _____
- ❑ Parking $_____
- ❑ Refund policy

   _____

   _____

Madison Blue Springs State Park

City: Lee   **County: Madison**

Plan your trip: https://www.floridastateparks.org/parks-and-trails/madison-blue-spring-state-park

Activities:

- ❑ Birding / Wildlife
- ❑ Fishing
- ❑ Guided tours
- ❑ Geo cache
- ❑ Hiking
- ❑ Horseback
- ❑ Hunting
- ❑ Snorkeling
- ❑ Trails
- ❑ Water access

Facilities:

- ❑ ADA
- ❑ Meeting hall
- ❑ Pavilions
- ❑ Picnic sites
- ❑ Restrooms
- ❑ Visitor center
- ❑
- ❑
- ❑
- ❑

Get the Facts

- ❑ Phone 850-971-5003
- ❑ Park Hours

  _____

- ❑ Reservations? ____Y ____N

  date made_____

- ❑ Open year 'round ___Y___N

  dates_____

- ❑ Distance from home

  miles: _____

  hours: _____

- ❑ Address or GPS

  _____

  _____

Date visited:

I went with:
_____

My favorite things:
_____
_____
_____
_____

Notes

Fees:

- ❑ Day Use $ _____
- ❑ Parking $_____
- ❑ Refund policy

  _____

  _____

Troy Spring State Park
City: Branford   County: Suwannee

Plan your trip: https://www.floridastateparks.org/parks-and-trails/troy-spring-state-park

Activities:

- ❑ Birding / Wildlife
- ❑ Fishing
- ❑ Guided tours
- ❑ Geo cache
- ❑ Hiking
- ❑ Horseback
- ❑ Hunting
- ❑ Snorkeling
- ❑ Trails
- ❑ Water access

Facilities:

- ❑ ADA
- ❑ Meeting hall
- ❑ Pavilions
- ❑ Picnic sites
- ❑ Restrooms
- ❑ Visitor center
- ❑
- ❑
- ❑
- ❑

Get the Facts

- ❑ Phone 386-935-4835
- ❑ Park Hours

  _____

- ❑ Reservations? ____Y ____N

  date made_____

- ❑ Open year 'round ___Y___N

  dates_____

- ❑ Distance from home

  miles: _____

  hours: _____

- ❑ Address or GPS

  _____

  _____

Date visited:

I went with:

_____

My favorite things:

_____

_____

_____

Notes

Fees:

- ❑ Day Use $ _____
- ❑ Parking $_____
- ❑ Refund policy

  _____

  _____

Wes Skiles Peacock Springs State Park
City: Live Oak   County: Suwannee

Plan your trip: https://www.floridastateparks.org/index.php/parks-and-trails/wes-skiles-peacock-springs-state-park

Activities:

- ❑ Birding / Wildlife
- ❑ Fishing
- ❑ Guided tours
- ❑ Geo cache
- ❑ Hiking
- ❑ Horseback
- ❑ Hunting
- ❑ Snorkeling
- ❑ Trails
- ❑ Water access

Facilities:

- ❑ ADA
- ❑ Meeting hall
- ❑ Pavilions
- ❑ Picnic sites
- ❑ Restrooms
- ❑ Visitor center
- ❑
- ❑
- ❑
- ❑

Get the Facts

- ❑ Phone 386-776-2194
- ❑ Park Hours

  _____

- ❑ Reservations? ____Y ____N

  date made_____

- ❑ Open year 'round ___Y___N

  dates_____

- ❑ Distance from home

  miles: _____

  hours: _____

- ❑ Address or GPS

  _____

  _____

Date visited:

I went with:
_____

My favorite things:
_____

_____

_____

Notes

Fees:

- ❑ Day Use $ _____
- ❑ Parking $_____
- ❑ Refund policy

  _____

  _____

Forest Capital Museum State Park
City: Perry   County: Taylor

Plan your trip: https://www.floridastateparks.org/index.php/parks-and-trails/forest-capital-museum-state-park

Activities:

- ❏ Birding / Wildlife
- ❏ Fishing
- ❏ Guided tours
- ❏ Geo cache
- ❏ Hiking
- ❏ Horseback
- ❏ Hunting
- ❏ Snorkeling
- ❏ Trails
- ❏ Water access

Facilities:

- ❏ ADA
- ❏ Meeting hall
- ❏ Pavilions
- ❏ Picnic sites
- ❏ Restrooms
- ❏ Visitor center
- ❏
- ❏
- ❏
- ❏

Get the Facts

- ❏ Phone 850-587-3227
- ❏ Park Hours

    _____

- ❏ Reservations? ____Y ____N

    date made_____

- ❏ Open year 'round ___Y___N

    dates_____

- ❏ Distance from home

    miles: _____

    hours: _____

- ❏ Address or GPS

    _____

    _____

Date visited:

I went with:
_____

My favorite things:
_____

_____

_____

Fees:

- ❏ Day Use $ _____
- ❏ Parking $_____
- ❏ Refund policy

    _____

    _____

Notes

San Marcos de Apalache Historic SP
City: St. Marks   County: Wakulla

Plan your trip: https://www.floridastateparks.org/index.php/parks-and-trails/san-marcos-de-apalache-historic-state-park

Activities:

- ❑ Birding / Wildlife
- ❑ Fishing
- ❑ Guided tours
- ❑ Geo cache
- ❑ Hiking
- ❑ Horseback
- ❑ Hunting
- ❑ Snorkeling
- ❑ Trails
- ❑ Water access

Facilities:

- ❑ ADA
- ❑ Meeting hall
- ❑ Pavilions
- ❑ Picnic sites
- ❑ Restrooms
- ❑ Visitor center
- ❑
- ❑
- ❑
- ❑

Get the Facts

- ❑ Phone 850-925-6216
- ❑ Park Hours

  _____

- ❑ Reservations? ____Y ____N

  date made_____

- ❑ Open year 'round ___Y ___N

  dates_____

- ❑ Distance from home

  miles: _____

  hours: _____

- ❑ Address or GPS

  _____

  _____

Date visited:

I went with:

_____

My favorite things:

_____

_____

_____

_____

Notes

Fees:

- ❑ Day Use $ _____
- ❑ Parking $_____
- ❑ Refund policy

  _____

  _____

Northeast

- Baker
- Clay
- Duval
- Flagler
- Nassau
- Putnam
- St. Johns

Mike Roess Gold Head Branch State Park
City: Keystone Heights   County: Clay

Plan your Trip https://www.floridastateparks.org/parks-and-trails/mike-roess-gold-head-branch-state-park

Activities:

- ❑ Beach Access
- ❑ Biking Trails
- ❑ Boating
- ❑ Campfire
- ❑ Caving
- ❑ Disc Golf
- ❑ Fishing
- ❑ Geo Cache
- ❑ Golf
- ❑ Hiking
- ❑ Horseback

- ❑ Hunting
- ❑ OHV
- ❑ Park Tours
- ❑ Rock Climbing
- ❑ Snorkeling
- ❑ Stargazing
- ❑ Swimming
- ❑ Viewpoint
- ❑ Wildlife & Birding
- ❑
- ❑

Facilities:

- ❑ ADA
- ❑ Gym
- ❑ Historic Sites
- ❑ Lodge
- ❑ Meeting Hall
- ❑ Pavilions
- ❑ Picnic sites
- ❑ Pool
- ❑ Restrooms

- ❑ Showers
- ❑ Visitor Center
- ❑ RV Camp
- ❑ Tent Camp
- ❑ Cabins
- ❑ Lodge Rooms
- ❑
- ❑
- ❑

Notes:

Get the Facts

- ❑ Phone: 352-473-4701
- ❑ Park Hours

  _____

- ❑ Reservations? ____Y ____N

  date made_____

- ❑ Open year 'round ___Y___N

  dates_____

- ❑ Check in time _____
- ❑ Check out time _____
- ❑ Dog friendly _____Y _____N
- ❑ Max RV length _____
- ❑ Distance from home

  miles: _____

  hours: _____

- ❑ Address_____

  _____

  _____

Fees:

- ❑ Day Use $ _____
- ❑ Camp Sites $_____
- ❑ RV Sites $ _____
- ❑ Refund policy

  _____

  _____

  _____

Make It Personal

Trip dates:

Why I went:

I went with:

How I got there: (circle all that apply) Plane   Train   Car   Bus   Bike   Hike   RV   MC

We stayed in (space, cabin, etc.)

The weather was: Sunny   Cloudy   Rainy   Stormy   Snowy   Foggy   Warm   Cold

Most relaxing day:

Something funny:

Someone we met:

Best story told:

The kids liked this:

The best food:

Games played:

Something disappointing:

Next time I'll do this differently:

George Crady Bridge Fishing Pier State Park

City: Jacksonville   County: Duval

Plan your Trip https://www.floridastateparks.org/parks-and-trails/george-crady-bridge-fishing-pier-state-park

Activities:

- ❑ Beach Access
- ❑ Biking Trails
- ❑ Boating
- ❑ Campfire
- ❑ Caving
- ❑ Disc Golf
- ❑ Fishing
- ❑ Geo Cache
- ❑ Golf
- ❑ Hiking
- ❑ Horseback

- ❑ Hunting
- ❑ OHV
- ❑ Park Tours
- ❑ Rock Climbing
- ❑ Snorkeling
- ❑ Stargazing
- ❑ Swimming
- ❑ Viewpoint
- ❑ Wildlife & Birding
- ❑
- ❑

Facilities:

- ❑ ADA
- ❑ Gym
- ❑ Historic Sites
- ❑ Lodge
- ❑ Meeting Hall
- ❑ Pavilions
- ❑ Picnic sites
- ❑ Pool
- ❑ Restrooms

- ❑ Showers
- ❑ Visitor Center
- ❑ RV Camp
- ❑ Tent Camp
- ❑ Cabins
- ❑ Lodge Rooms
- ❑
- ❑
- ❑

Notes:

Get the Facts

- ❑ Phone: 904-251-2320
- ❑ Park Hours

  _____

- ❑ Reservations? ____Y ____N

  date made_____

- ❑ Open year 'round ___Y___N

  dates_____

- ❑ Check in time _____
- ❑ Check out time _____
- ❑ Dog friendly _____Y _____N
- ❑ Max RV length _____
- ❑ Distance from home

  miles: _____

  hours: _____

- ❑ Address_____

  _____

  _____

Fees:

- ❑ Day Use $ _____
- ❑ Camp Sites $_____
- ❑ RV Sites $ _____
- ❑ Refund policy

  _____

  _____

  _____

Make It Personal

Trip dates:

Why I went:

I went with:

How I got there: (circle all that apply) Plane   Train   Car   Bus   Bike   Hike   RV   MC

We stayed in (space, cabin, etc.)

The weather was: Sunny   Cloudy   Rainy   Stormy   Snowy   Foggy   Warm   Cold

Most relaxing day:

Something funny:

Someone we met:

Best story told:

The kids liked this:

The best food:

Games played:

Something disappointing:

Next time I'll do this differently:

Little Talbot Island State Park
City: Jacksonville   County: Duval

Plan your Trip https://www.floridastateparks.org/parks-and-trails/little-talbot-island-state-park

Activities:

- ❑ Beach Access
- ❑ Biking Trails
- ❑ Boating
- ❑ Campfire
- ❑ Caving
- ❑ Disc Golf
- ❑ Fishing
- ❑ Geo Cache
- ❑ Golf
- ❑ Hiking
- ❑ Horseback

- ❑ Hunting
- ❑ OHV
- ❑ Park Tours
- ❑ Rock Climbing
- ❑ Snorkeling
- ❑ Stargazing
- ❑ Swimming
- ❑ Viewpoint
- ❑ Wildlife & Birding
- ❑
- ❑

Facilities:

- ❑ ADA
- ❑ Gym
- ❑ Historic Sites
- ❑ Lodge
- ❑ Meeting Hall
- ❑ Pavilions
- ❑ Picnic sites
- ❑ Pool
- ❑ Restrooms

- ❑ Showers
- ❑ Visitor Center
- ❑ RV Camp
- ❑ Tent Camp
- ❑ Cabins
- ❑ Lodge Rooms
- ❑
- ❑
- ❑

Notes:

Get the Facts

- ❑ Phone: 904-251-2320
- ❑ Park Hours

  _____

- ❑ Reservations? ____Y ____N

  date made_____

- ❑ Open year 'round ___Y___N

  dates_____

- ❑ Check in time _____
- ❑ Check out time _____
- ❑ Dog friendly _____Y _____N
- ❑ Max RV length _____
- ❑ Distance from home

  miles: _____

  hours: _____

- ❑ Address_____

  _____

  _____

Fees:

- ❑ Day Use $ _____
- ❑ Camp Sites $_____
- ❑ RV Sites $ _____
- ❑ Refund policy

  _____

  _____

  _____

100

Make It Personal

Trip dates:

Why I went:

I went with:

How I got there: (circle all that apply) Plane   Train   Car   Bus   Bike   Hike   RV   MC

We stayed in (space, cabin, etc.)

The weather was: Sunny   Cloudy   Rainy   Stormy   Snowy   Foggy   Warm   Cold

Most relaxing day:

Something funny:

Someone we met:

Best story told:

The kids liked this:

The best food:

Games played:

Something disappointing:

Next time I'll do this differently:

Gamble Rogers Memorial State Rec. Area at Flagler Beach

City: Flagler Beach County: Flagler

Plan your Trip https://www.floridastateparks.org/parks-and-trails/gamble-rogers-memorial-state-recreation-area-flagler-beach

Activities:

- ❑ Beach Access
- ❑ Biking Trails
- ❑ Boating
- ❑ Campfire
- ❑ Caving
- ❑ Disc Golf
- ❑ Fishing
- ❑ Geo Cache
- ❑ Golf
- ❑ Hiking
- ❑ Horseback

- ❑ Hunting
- ❑ OHV
- ❑ Park Tours
- ❑ Rock Climbing
- ❑ Snorkeling
- ❑ Stargazing
- ❑ Swimming
- ❑ Viewpoint
- ❑ Wildlife & Birding
- ❑
- ❑

Facilities:

- ❑ ADA
- ❑ Gym
- ❑ Historic Sites
- ❑ Lodge
- ❑ Meeting Hall
- ❑ Pavilions
- ❑ Picnic sites
- ❑ Pool
- ❑ Restrooms

- ❑ Showers
- ❑ Visitor Center
- ❑ RV Camp
- ❑ Tent Camp
- ❑ Cabins
- ❑ Lodge Rooms
- ❑
- ❑
- ❑

Notes:

Get the Facts

- ❑ Phone: 386-517-2086
- ❑ Park Hours

  _____

- ❑ Reservations? ____Y ____N

  date made_____

- ❑ Open year 'round ___Y___N

  dates_____

- ❑ Check in time _____
- ❑ Check out time _____
- ❑ Dog friendly _____Y _____N
- ❑ Max RV length _____
- ❑ Distance from home

  miles: _____

  hours: _____

- ❑ Address_____

  _____

  _____

Fees:

- ❑ Day Use $ _____
- ❑ Camp Sites $_____
- ❑ RV Sites $ _____
- ❑ Refund policy

  _____

  _____

  _____

Make It Personal

Trip dates:

Why I went:

I went with:

How I got there: (circle all that apply) Plane   Train   Car   Bus   Bike   Hike   RV   MC

We stayed in (space, cabin, etc.)

The weather was: Sunny   Cloudy   Rainy   Stormy   Snowy   Foggy   Warm   Cold

Most relaxing day:

Something funny:

Someone we met:

Best story told:

The kids liked this:

The best food:

Games played:

Something disappointing:

Next time I'll do this differently:

Fort Clinch State Park
City: Fernandina Beach   County: Nassau

Plan your Trip https://www.floridastateparks.org/fortclinch

Activities:

- ❏ Beach Access
- ❏ Biking Trails
- ❏ Boating
- ❏ Campfire
- ❏ Caving
- ❏ Disc Golf
- ❏ Fishing
- ❏ Geo Cache
- ❏ Golf
- ❏ Hiking
- ❏ Horseback
- ❏ Hunting
- ❏ OHV
- ❏ Park Tours
- ❏ Rock Climbing
- ❏ Snorkeling
- ❏ Stargazing
- ❏ Swimming
- ❏ Viewpoint
- ❏ Wildlife & Birding
- ❏
- ❏

Facilities:

- ❏ ADA
- ❏ Gym
- ❏ Historic Sites
- ❏ Lodge
- ❏ Meeting Hall
- ❏ Pavilions
- ❏ Picnic sites
- ❏ Pool
- ❏ Restrooms
- ❏ Showers
- ❏ Visitor Center
- ❏ RV Camp
- ❏ Tent Camp
- ❏ Cabins
- ❏ Lodge Rooms
- ❏
- ❏
- ❏

Notes:

Get the Facts

- ❏ Phone: 904-277-7274
- ❏ Park Hours

  _____

- ❏ Reservations? ____Y ____N

  date made_____

- ❏ Open year 'round ___Y___N

  dates_____

- ❏ Check in time _____
- ❏ Check out time _____
- ❏ Dog friendly _____Y _____N
- ❏ Max RV length _____
- ❏ Distance from home

  miles: _____

  hours: _____

- ❏ Address_____

  _____

  _____

Fees:

- ❏ Day Use $ _____
- ❏ Camp Sites $_____
- ❏ RV Sites $ _____
- ❏ Refund policy

  _____

  _____

  _____

Make It Personal

Trip dates: _____

Why I went: _____

I went with: _____

How I got there: (circle all that apply) Plane   Train   Car   Bus   Bike   Hike   RV   MC

We stayed in (space, cabin, etc.) _____

The weather was: Sunny   Cloudy   Rainy   Stormy   Snowy   Foggy   Warm   Cold

Most relaxing day: _____

_____

Something funny: _____

_____

Someone we met: _____

_____

Best story told: _____

_____

The kids liked this: _____

The best food: _____

Games played: _____

Something disappointing: _____

Next time I'll do this differently: _____

_____

105

Eureka West Recreation Area
City: Fort McCoy   County: Putnam

Plan your Trip https://www.floridastateparks.org/parks-and-trails/eureka-west-recreation-area

Activities:

- ❑ Beach Access
- ❑ Biking Trails
- ❑ Boating
- ❑ Campfire
- ❑ Caving
- ❑ Disc Golf
- ❑ Fishing
- ❑ Geo Cache
- ❑ Golf
- ❑ Hiking
- ❑ Horseback

- ❑ Hunting
- ❑ OHV
- ❑ Park Tours
- ❑ Rock Climbing
- ❑ Snorkeling
- ❑ Stargazing
- ❑ Swimming
- ❑ Viewpoint
- ❑ Wildlife & Birding
- ❑
- ❑

Facilities:

- ❑ ADA
- ❑ Gym
- ❑ Historic Sites
- ❑ Lodge
- ❑ Meeting Hall
- ❑ Pavilions
- ❑ Picnic sites
- ❑ Pool
- ❑ Restrooms

- ❑ Showers
- ❑ Visitor Center
- ❑ RV Camp
- ❑ Tent Camp
- ❑ Cabins
- ❑ Lodge Rooms
- ❑
- ❑
- ❑

Notes:

Get the Facts

- ❑ Phone: 352-236-7143
- ❑ Park Hours

  _____

- ❑ Reservations? ____Y ____N

  date made_____

- ❑ Open year 'round ___Y___N

  dates_____

- ❑ Check in time _____
- ❑ Check out time _____
- ❑ Dog friendly _____Y _____N
- ❑ Max RV length _____
- ❑ Distance from home

  miles: _____

  hours: _____

- ❑ Address_____

  _____

  _____

Fees:

- ❑ Day Use $ _____
- ❑ Camp Sites $_____
- ❑ RV Sites $ _____
- ❑ Refund policy

  _____

  _____

  _____

Make It Personal

Trip dates:

Why I went:

I went with:

How I got there: (circle all that apply) Plane   Train   Car   Bus   Bike   Hike   RV   MC

We stayed in (space, cabin, etc.)

The weather was: Sunny   Cloudy   Rainy   Stormy   Snowy   Foggy   Warm   Cold

Most relaxing day:

Something funny:

Someone we met:

Best story told:

The kids liked this:

The best food:

Games played:

Something disappointing:

Next time I'll do this differently:

Rodman Campground
City: Palatka County: Putnam

Plan your Trip https://www.floridastateparks.org/parks-and-trails/rodman-campground

Activities:

- ❑ Beach Access
- ❑ Biking Trails
- ❑ Boating
- ❑ Campfire
- ❑ Caving
- ❑ Disc Golf
- ❑ Fishing
- ❑ Geo Cache
- ❑ Golf
- ❑ Hiking
- ❑ Horseback

- ❑ Hunting
- ❑ OHV
- ❑ Park Tours
- ❑ Rock Climbing
- ❑ Snorkeling
- ❑ Stargazing
- ❑ Swimming
- ❑ Viewpoint
- ❑ Wildlife & Birding
- ❑
- ❑

Facilities:

- ❑ ADA
- ❑ Gym
- ❑ Historic Sites
- ❑ Lodge
- ❑ Meeting Hall
- ❑ Pavilions
- ❑ Picnic sites
- ❑ Pool
- ❑ Restrooms

- ❑ Showers
- ❑ Visitor Center
- ❑ RV Camp
- ❑ Tent Camp
- ❑ Cabins
- ❑ Lodge Rooms
- ❑
- ❑
- ❑

Notes:

Get the Facts

- ❑ Phone: 386-326-2846
- ❑ Park Hours

  _____

- ❑ Reservations? ____Y ____N

  date made_____

- ❑ Open year 'round ___Y___N

  dates_____

- ❑ Check in time _____
- ❑ Check out time _____
- ❑ Dog friendly _____Y _____N
- ❑ Max RV length _____
- ❑ Distance from home

  miles: _____

  hours: _____

- ❑ Address_____

  _____

  _____

Fees:

- ❑ Day Use $ _____
- ❑ Camp Sites $_____
- ❑ RV Sites $ _____
- ❑ Refund policy

  _____

  _____

  _____

Make It Personal

Trip dates: _____

Why I went: _____

I went with: _____

How I got there: (circle all that apply) Plane   Train   Car   Bus   Bike   Hike   RV   MC

We stayed in (space, cabin, etc.) _____

_____

The weather was: Sunny   Cloudy   Rainy   Stormy   Snowy   Foggy   Warm   Cold

Most relaxing day: _____

_____

Something funny: _____

_____

Someone we met: _____

_____

Best story told: _____

_____

The kids liked this: _____

The best food: _____

_____

Games played: _____

_____

Something disappointing: _____

_____

Next time I'll do this differently: _____

_____

Anastasia State Park
City: St. Augustine   County: St. Johns

Plan your Trip https://www.floridastateparks.org/index.php/anastasia

Activities:

- ❑ Beach Access
- ❑ Biking Trails
- ❑ Boating
- ❑ Campfire
- ❑ Caving
- ❑ Disc Golf
- ❑ Fishing
- ❑ Geo Cache
- ❑ Golf
- ❑ Hiking
- ❑ Horseback

- ❑ Hunting
- ❑ OHV
- ❑ Park Tours
- ❑ Rock Climbing
- ❑ Snorkeling
- ❑ Stargazing
- ❑ Swimming
- ❑ Viewpoint
- ❑ Wildlife & Birding
- ❑
- ❑

Facilities:

- ❑ ADA
- ❑ Gym
- ❑ Historic Sites
- ❑ Lodge
- ❑ Meeting Hall
- ❑ Pavilions
- ❑ Picnic sites
- ❑ Pool
- ❑ Restrooms

- ❑ Showers
- ❑ Visitor Center
- ❑ RV Camp
- ❑ Tent Camp
- ❑ Cabins
- ❑ Lodge Rooms
- ❑
- ❑
- ❑

Notes:

Get the Facts

- ❑ Phone: 904-461-2033
- ❑ Park Hours

  _____

- ❑ Reservations? ____Y ____N

  date made_____

- ❑ Open year 'round ___Y___N

  dates_____

- ❑ Check in time _____
- ❑ Check out time _____
- ❑ Dog friendly _____Y _____N
- ❑ Max RV length _____
- ❑ Distance from home

  miles: _____

  hours: _____

- ❑ Address_____

  _____

  _____

Fees:

- ❑ Day Use $ _____
- ❑ Camp Sites $_____
- ❑ RV Sites $ _____
- ❑ Refund policy

  _____

  _____

  _____

Make It Personal

Trip dates: _____

Why I went: _____

I went with: _____

How I got there: (circle all that apply) Plane   Train   Car   Bus   Bike   Hike   RV   MC

We stayed in (space, cabin, etc.) _____

The weather was: Sunny   Cloudy   Rainy   Stormy   Snowy   Foggy   Warm   Cold

Most relaxing day: _____

Something funny: _____

Someone we met: _____

Best story told: _____

The kids liked this: _____

The best food: _____

Games played: _____

Something disappointing: _____

Next time I'll do this differently: _____

Faver-Dykes State Park
City: St. Augustine   County: St. Johns

Plan your Trip https://www.floridastateparks.org/parks-and-trails/faver-dykes-state-park

Activities:

- ❑ Beach Access
- ❑ Biking Trails
- ❑ Boating
- ❑ Campfire
- ❑ Caving
- ❑ Disc Golf
- ❑ Fishing
- ❑ Geo Cache
- ❑ Golf
- ❑ Hiking
- ❑ Horseback

- ❑ Hunting
- ❑ OHV
- ❑ Park Tours
- ❑ Rock Climbing
- ❑ Snorkeling
- ❑ Stargazing
- ❑ Swimming
- ❑ Viewpoint
- ❑ Wildlife & Birding
- ❑
- ❑

Facilities:

- ❑ ADA
- ❑ Gym
- ❑ Historic Sites
- ❑ Lodge
- ❑ Meeting Hall
- ❑ Pavilions
- ❑ Picnic sites
- ❑ Pool
- ❑ Restrooms

- ❑ Showers
- ❑ Visitor Center
- ❑ RV Camp
- ❑ Tent Camp
- ❑ Cabins
- ❑ Lodge Rooms
- ❑
- ❑
- ❑

Notes:

Get the Facts

- ❑ Phone: 904-794-0997
- ❑ Park Hours

  _____

- ❑ Reservations? ____Y ____N

  date made_____

- ❑ Open year 'round ___Y___N

  dates_____

- ❑ Check in time _____
- ❑ Check out time _____
- ❑ Dog friendly _____Y _____N
- ❑ Max RV length _____
- ❑ Distance from home

  miles: _____

  hours: _____

- ❑ Address_____

  _____

  _____

Fees:

- ❑ Day Use $ _____
- ❑ Camp Sites $_____
- ❑ RV Sites $ _____
- ❑ Refund policy

  _____

  _____

  _____

112

Make It Personal

Trip dates:

Why I went:

I went with:

How I got there: (circle all that apply) Plane   Train   Car   Bus   Bike   Hike   RV   MC

We stayed in (space, cabin, etc.)

The weather was: Sunny   Cloudy   Rainy   Stormy   Snowy   Foggy   Warm   Cold

Most relaxing day:

Something funny:

Someone we met:

Best story told:

The kids liked this:

The best food:

Games played:

Something disappointing:

Next time I'll do this differently:

Olustee Battlefield State Park
City: Olustee   County: Baker

Plan your trip: https://www.floridastateparks.org/parks-and-trails/olustee-battlefield-historic-state-park

Activities:

- ❏ Birding / Wildlife
- ❏ Fishing
- ❏ Guided tours
- ❏ Geo cache
- ❏ Hiking
- ❏ Horseback
- ❏ Hunting
- ❏ Snorkeling
- ❏ Trails
- ❏ Water access

Facilities:

- ❏ ADA
- ❏ Meeting hall
- ❏ Pavilions
- ❏ Picnic sites
- ❏ Restrooms
- ❏ Visitor center
- ❏
- ❏
- ❏
- ❏

Get the Facts

- ❏ Phone 386-758-0400
- ❏ Park Hours

  _____

- ❏ Reservations? ____Y ____N

  date made_____

- ❏ Open year 'round ___Y___N

  dates_____

- ❏ Distance from home

  miles: _____

  hours: _____

- ❏ Address or GPS

  _____

  _____

Date visited:

I went with:

_____

My favorite things:

_____

_____

_____

Notes

Fees:

- ❏ Day Use $ _____
- ❏ Parking $_____
- ❏ Refund policy

  _____

  _____

Big Talbot Island State Park
City: Jacksonville   County: Duval

Plan your trip https://www.floridastateparks.org/index.php/parks-and-trails/big-talbot-island-state-park

Activities:

- ❏ Birding / Wildlife
- ❏ Fishing
- ❏ Guided tours
- ❏ Geo cache
- ❏ Hiking
- ❏ Horseback
- ❏ Hunting
- ❏ Snorkeling
- ❏ Trails
- ❏ Water access

Facilities:

- ❏ ADA
- ❏ Meeting hall
- ❏ Pavilions
- ❏ Picnic sites
- ❏ Restrooms
- ❏ Visitor center
- ❏
- ❏
- ❏
- ❏

Get the Facts

- ❏ Phone 904-251-2320
- ❏ Park Hours

  _____

- ❏ Reservations? ____Y ____N

  date made_____

- ❏ Open year 'round ___Y___N

  dates_____

- ❏ Distance from home

  miles: _____

  hours: _____

- ❏ Address or GPS

  _____

  _____

Date visited:

I went with: _____

My favorite things:
_____
_____
_____

Notes

Fees:

- ❏ Day Use $ _____
- ❏ Parking $_____
- ❏ Refund policy

  _____

  _____

115

Fort George Island Cultural State Park
City: Jacksonville   County: Duval

Plan your trip https://www.floridastateparks.org/parks-and-trails/fort-george-island-cultural-state-park

Activities:

❑ Birding / Wildlife
❑ Fishing
❑ Guided tours
❑ Geo cache
❑ Hiking
❑ Horseback
❑ Hunting
❑ Snorkeling
❑ Trails
❑ Water access

Facilities:

❑ ADA
❑ Meeting hall
❑ Pavilions
❑ Picnic sites
❑ Restrooms
❑ Visitor center
❑
❑
❑
❑

Get the Facts

❑ Phone 904-251-2320
❑ Park Hours

_____

❑ Reservations? ____Y ____N

date made_____

❑ Open year 'round ___Y___N

dates_____

❑ Distance from home

miles: _____

hours: _____

❑ Address or GPS

_____

_____

Date visited:

I went with:
_____

My favorite things:
_____

_____

_____

Fees:

❑ Day Use $ _____
❑ Parking $_____
❑ Refund policy

_____

_____

Notes

Pumpkin Hill Creek Preserve State Park
City: Jacksonville   County: Duval

Plan your trip https://www.floridastateparks.org/parks-and-trails/pumpkin-hill-creek-preserve-state-park

Activities:

- ❑ Birding / Wildlife
- ❑ Fishing
- ❑ Guided tours
- ❑ Geo cache
- ❑ Hiking
- ❑ Horseback
- ❑ Hunting
- ❑ Snorkeling
- ❑ Trails
- ❑ Water access

Facilities:

- ❑ ADA
- ❑ Meeting hall
- ❑ Pavilions
- ❑ Picnic sites
- ❑ Restrooms
- ❑ Visitor center
- ❑
- ❑
- ❑
- ❑

Get the Facts

- ❑ Phone 904-696-5980
- ❑ Park Hours

_____

- ❑ Reservations? ____Y ____N

date made_____

- ❑ Open year 'round ___Y___N

dates_____

- ❑ Distance from home

miles: _____

hours: _____

- ❑ Address or GPS

_____

_____

Date visited:

I went with:

_____

My favorite things:

_____

_____

_____

Notes

Fees:

- ❑ Day Use $ _____
- ❑ Parking $_____
- ❑ Refund policy

_____

_____

Yellow Bluff Fort Historic State Park

City: Jacksonville   County: Duval

Plan your trip https://www.floridastateparks.org/parks-and-trails/yellow-bluff-fort-historic-state-park

Activities:

- ❑ Birding / Wildlife
- ❑ Fishing
- ❑ Guided tours
- ❑ Geo cache
- ❑ Hiking
- ❑ Horseback
- ❑ Hunting
- ❑ Snorkeling
- ❑ Trails
- ❑ Water access

Facilities:

- ❑ ADA
- ❑ Meeting hall
- ❑ Pavilions
- ❑ Picnic sites
- ❑ Restrooms
- ❑ Visitor center
- ❑
- ❑
- ❑
- ❑

Get the Facts

- ❑ Phone 904-251-2320
- ❑ Park Hours

_____

- ❑ Reservations? ____Y ____N

date made_____

- ❑ Open year 'round ___Y___N

dates_____

- ❑ Distance from home

miles: _____

hours: _____

- ❑ Address or GPS

_____

_____

Date visited:

I went with:
_____

My favorite things:
_____

_____

_____

Notes

Fees:

- ❑ Day Use $ _____
- ❑ Parking $_____
- ❑ Refund policy

_____

_____

Bulow Plantation Ruins Historic SP
City: Flagler Beach   County: Flagler

Plan your trip https://www.floridastateparks.org/parks-and-trails/bulow-plantation-ruins-historic-state-park

Activities:

- ❏ Birding / Wildlife
- ❏ Fishing
- ❏ Guided tours
- ❏ Geo cache
- ❏ Hiking
- ❏ Horseback
- ❏ Hunting
- ❏ Snorkeling
- ❏ Trails
- ❏ Water access

Facilities:

- ❏ ADA
- ❏ Meeting hall
- ❏ Pavilions
- ❏ Picnic sites
- ❏ Restrooms
- ❏ Visitor center
- ❏
- ❏
- ❏
- ❏

Get the Facts

- ❏ Phone 386-517-2084
- ❏ Park Hours

  _____

- ❏ Reservations? ____Y ____N

  date made_____

- ❏ Open year 'round ___Y___N

  dates_____

- ❏ Distance from home

  miles: _____

  hours: _____

- ❏ Address or GPS

  _____

  _____

Date visited:

I went with:

_____

My favorite things:

_____

_____

_____

Notes

Fees:

- ❏ Day Use $ _____
- ❏ Parking $_____
- ❏ Refund policy

  _____

  _____

Washington Oaks Garden State Park

City: Palm Coast   County: Flagler

Plan your trip https://www.floridastateparks.org/index.php/parks-and-trails/washington-oaks-gardens-state-park

Activities:

- ❑ Birding / Wildlife
- ❑ Fishing
- ❑ Guided tours
- ❑ Geo cache
- ❑ Hiking
- ❑ Horseback
- ❑ Hunting
- ❑ Snorkeling
- ❑ Trails
- ❑ Water access

Facilities:

- ❑ ADA
- ❑ Meeting hall
- ❑ Pavilions
- ❑ Picnic sites
- ❑ Restrooms
- ❑ Visitor center
- ❑
- ❑
- ❑
- ❑

Get the Facts

- ❑ Phone 386-446-6780
- ❑ Park Hours

  _____

- ❑ Reservations? ____Y ____N

  date made_____

- ❑ Open year 'round ___Y___N

  dates_____

- ❑ Distance from home

  miles: _____

  hours: _____

- ❑ Address or GPS

  _____

  _____

Date visited:

I went with:
_____

My favorite things:
_____

_____

_____

Notes

Fees:

- ❑ Day Use $ _____
- ❑ Parking $_____
- ❑ Refund policy

  _____

  _____

120

Ferandina Plaza Historic State Park
City: Fernandina Beach   County: Nassau

Plan your trip https://www.floridastateparks.org/parks-and-trails/fernandina-plaza-historic-state-park

Activities:

- ❏ Birding / Wildlife
- ❏ Fishing
- ❏ Guided tours
- ❏ Geo cache
- ❏ Hiking
- ❏ Horseback
- ❏ Hunting
- ❏ Snorkeling
- ❏ Trails
- ❏ Water access

Facilities:

- ❏ ADA
- ❏ Meeting hall
- ❏ Pavilions
- ❏ Picnic sites
- ❏ Restrooms
- ❏ Visitor center
- ❏
- ❏
- ❏
- ❏

Get the Facts

- ❏ Phone 904-277-7274
- ❏ Park Hours

    _____

- ❏ Reservations? ____Y ____N

    date made_____

- ❏ Open year 'round ___Y___N

    dates_____

- ❏ Distance from home

    miles: _____

    hours: _____

- ❏ Address or GPS

    _____

    _____

Date visited:

I went with:

_____

My favorite things:

_____

_____

_____

Fees:

- ❏ Day Use $ _____
- ❏ Parking $_____
- ❏ Refund policy

    _____

    _____

Notes

Amelia Island State Park
City: Jacksonville   County: Nassau

Plan your trip https://www.floridastateparks.org/parks-and-trails/amelia-island-state-park

Activities:

- ❑ Birding / Wildlife
- ❑ Fishing
- ❑ Guided tours
- ❑ Geo cache
- ❑ Hiking
- ❑ Horseback
- ❑ Hunting
- ❑ Snorkeling
- ❑ Trails
- ❑ Water access

Facilities:

- ❑ ADA
- ❑ Meeting hall
- ❑ Pavilions
- ❑ Picnic sites
- ❑ Restrooms
- ❑ Visitor center
- ❑
- ❑
- ❑
- ❑

Get the Facts

- ❑ Phone 904-251-2320
- ❑ Park Hours

_____

- ❑ Reservations? ____Y ____N

date made_____

- ❑ Open year 'round ___Y___N

dates_____

- ❑ Distance from home

miles: _____

hours: _____

- ❑ Address or GPS

_____

_____

Date visited:

I went with:
_____

My favorite things:
_____

_____

_____

Notes

Fees:

- ❑ Day Use $ _____
- ❑ Parking $_____
- ❑ Refund policy

_____

_____

Kenwood Recreation Area

City: Interlachen   County: Putnam

Plan your trip https://www.floridastateparks.org/index.php/parks-and-trails/kenwood-recreation-area

Activities:

- ❑ Birding / Wildlife
- ❑ Fishing
- ❑ Guided tours
- ❑ Geo cache
- ❑ Hiking
- ❑ Horseback
- ❑ Hunting
- ❑ Snorkeling
- ❑ Trails
- ❑ Water access

Facilities:

- ❑ ADA
- ❑ Meeting hall
- ❑ Pavilions
- ❑ Picnic sites
- ❑ Restrooms
- ❑ Visitor center
- ❑
- ❑
- ❑
- ❑

Get the Facts

- ❑ Phone 352-236-7143
- ❑ Park Hours

  _____

- ❑ Reservations? ____Y ____N

  date made_____

- ❑ Open year 'round ___Y___N

  dates_____

- ❑ Distance from home

  miles: _____

  hours: _____

- ❑ Address or GPS

  _____

  _____

Date visited:

I went with:

_____

My favorite things:

_____

_____

_____

Notes

Fees:

- ❑ Day Use $ _____
- ❑ Parking $_____
- ❑ Refund policy

  _____

  _____

Ravine Gardens State Park
City: Palatka   County: Putnam

Plan your trip https://www.floridastateparks.org/parks-and-trails/ravine-gardens-state-park

Activities:

- ❑ Birding / Wildlife
- ❑ Fishing
- ❑ Guided tours
- ❑ Geo cache
- ❑ Hiking
- ❑ Horseback
- ❑ Hunting
- ❑ Snorkeling
- ❑ Trails
- ❑ Water access

Facilities:

- ❑ ADA
- ❑ Meeting hall
- ❑ Pavilions
- ❑ Picnic sites
- ❑ Restrooms
- ❑ Visitor center
- ❑
- ❑
- ❑
- ❑

Get the Facts

- ❑ Phone 386-329-3721
- ❑ Park Hours

_____

- ❑ Reservations? ____Y ____N

date made_____

- ❑ Open year 'round ___Y___N

dates_____

- ❑ Distance from home

miles: _____

hours: _____

- ❑ Address or GPS

_____

_____

Date visited:

I went with:
_____

My favorite things:
_____

_____

_____

Notes

Fees:

- ❑ Day Use $ _____
- ❑ Parking $_____
- ❑ Refund policy

_____

_____

Rodman Recreation Area
City: Palatka   County: Putnam

Plan your trip https://www.floridastateparks.org/parks-and-trails/rodman-recreation-area

Activities:

- ❑ Birding / Wildlife
- ❑ Fishing
- ❑ Guided tours
- ❑ Geo cache
- ❑ Hiking
- ❑ Horseback
- ❑ Hunting
- ❑ Snorkeling
- ❑ Trails
- ❑ Water access

Facilities:

- ❑ ADA
- ❑ Meeting hall
- ❑ Pavilions
- ❑ Picnic sites
- ❑ Restrooms
- ❑ Visitor center
- ❑
- ❑
- ❑
- ❑

Get the Facts

- ❑ Phone 352-236-7143
- ❑ Park Hours

_____

- ❑ Reservations? ____Y ____N

  date made_____

- ❑ Open year 'round ___Y___N

  dates_____

- ❑ Distance from home

  miles: _____

  hours: _____

- ❑ Address or GPS

  _____

  _____

Date visited:

I went with:

_____

My favorite things:

_____

_____

_____

Notes

Fees:

- ❑ Day Use $ _____
- ❑ Parking $_____
- ❑ Refund policy

  _____

  _____

Dunns Creek State Park
City: Pomona Park   County: Putnam

Plan your trip https://www.floridastateparks.org/index.php/DunnsCreek

Activities:

- ❏ Birding / Wildlife
- ❏ Fishing
- ❏ Guided tours
- ❏ Geo cache
- ❏ Hiking
- ❏ Horseback
- ❏ Hunting
- ❏ Snorkeling
- ❏ Trails
- ❏ Water access

Facilities:

- ❏ ADA
- ❏ Meeting hall
- ❏ Pavilions
- ❏ Picnic sites
- ❏ Restrooms
- ❏ Visitor center
- ❏
- ❏
- ❏
- ❏

Get the Facts

- ❏ Phone 386-329-3721
- ❏ Park Hours

    _____

- ❏ Reservations? ____Y ____N

    date made_____

- ❏ Open year 'round ___Y___N

    dates_____

- ❏ Distance from home

    miles: _____

    hours: _____

- ❏ Address or GPS

    _____

    _____

Date visited:

I went with:

_____

My favorite things:

_____

_____

_____

Notes

Fees:

- ❏ Day Use $ _____
- ❏ Parking $_____
- ❏ Refund policy

    _____

    _____

Fort Mose Historic State Park
City: St. Augustine   County: St. Johns

Plan your trip https://www.floridastateparks.org/parks-and-trails/fort-mose-historic-state-park

Activities:

- ❑ Birding / Wildlife
- ❑ Fishing
- ❑ Guided tours
- ❑ Geo cache
- ❑ Hiking
- ❑ Horseback
- ❑ Hunting
- ❑ Snorkeling
- ❑ Trails
- ❑ Water access

Facilities:

- ❑ ADA
- ❑ Meeting hall
- ❑ Pavilions
- ❑ Picnic sites
- ❑ Restrooms
- ❑ Visitor center
- ❑
- ❑
- ❑
- ❑

Get the Facts

- ❑ Phone 904-823-2232
- ❑ Park Hours

_____

- ❑ Reservations? ____Y ____N

date made_____

- ❑ Open year 'round ___Y___N

dates_____

- ❑ Distance from home

miles: _____

hours: _____

- ❑ Address or GPS

_____

_____

Date visited:

I went with:
_____

My favorite things:
_____

_____

_____

Notes

Fees:

- ❑ Day Use $ _____
- ❑ Parking $_____
- ❑ Refund policy

_____

_____

National Wildlife Refuges in Florida

There are 20 National Wildlife Refuges in Florida. Why not add these to your bucket list?

- ❑ Caloosahatchee National Wildlife Refuge,
- ❑ Cedar Keys National Wildlife Refuge,
- ❑ Chassahowitzka National Wildlife Refuge,
- ❑ Crocodile Lake National Wildlife Refuge
- ❑ Egmont Key National Wildlife Refuge
- ❑ Great White Heron National Wildlife Refuge
- ❑ Hobe Sound National Wildlife Refuge
- ❑ Island Bay National Wildlife Refuge
- ❑ Key West National Wildlife Refuge
- ❑ Lake Woodruff National Wildlife Refuge
- ❑ Lower Suwannee National Wildlife Refuge
- ❑ Loxahatchee National Wildlife Refuge
- ❑ Matlacha Pass National Wildlife Refuge
- ❑ Merritt Island National Wildlife Refuge
- ❑ Passage Key National Wildlife Refuge
- ❑ Pelican Island National Wildlife Refuge
- ❑ Pine Island National Wildlife Refuge
- ❑ Pinellas National Wildlife Refuge
- ❑ Saint Johns National Wildlife Refuge
- ❑ Saint Marks National Wildlife Refuge

Central West

- Citrus
- Hernando
- Hillsborough
- Manatee
- Pasco
- Pinellas
- Sarasota

Fort Cooper State Park
City: Inverness   County: Citrus

Plan your Trip https://www.floridastateparks.org/parks-and-trails/fort-cooper-state-park

Activities:

- ❑ Beach Access
- ❑ Biking Trails
- ❑ Boating
- ❑ Campfire
- ❑ Caving
- ❑ Disc Golf
- ❑ Fishing
- ❑ Geo Cache
- ❑ Golf
- ❑ Hiking
- ❑ Horseback

- ❑ Hunting
- ❑ OHV
- ❑ Park Tours
- ❑ Rock Climbing
- ❑ Snorkeling
- ❑ Stargazing
- ❑ Swimming
- ❑ Viewpoint
- ❑ Wildlife & Birding
- ❑
- ❑

Facilities:

- ❑ ADA
- ❑ Gym
- ❑ Historic Sites
- ❑ Lodge
- ❑ Meeting Hall
- ❑ Pavilions
- ❑ Picnic sites
- ❑ Pool
- ❑ Restrooms

- ❑ Showers
- ❑ Visitor Center
- ❑ RV Camp
- ❑ Tent Camp
- ❑ Cabins
- ❑ Lodge Rooms
- ❑
- ❑
- ❑

Notes:

Get the Facts

- ❑ Phone: 352-726-0315
- ❑ Park Hours

  _____

- ❑ Reservations? ____Y ____N

  date made_____

- ❑ Open year 'round ___Y___N

  dates_____

- ❑ Check in time _____
- ❑ Check out time _____
- ❑ Dog friendly _____Y _____N
- ❑ Max RV length _____
- ❑ Distance from home

  miles: _____

  hours: _____

- ❑ Address_____

  _____

  _____

Fees:

- ❑ Day Use $ _____
- ❑ Camp Sites $_____
- ❑ RV Sites $ _____
- ❑ Refund policy

  _____

  _____

  _____

Make It Personal

Trip dates:

Why I went:

I went with:

How I got there: (circle all that apply) Plane   Train   Car   Bus   Bike   Hike   RV   MC

We stayed in (space, cabin, etc.)

The weather was: Sunny   Cloudy   Rainy   Stormy   Snowy   Foggy   Warm   Cold

Most relaxing day:

Something funny:

Someone we met:

Best story told:

The kids liked this:

The best food:

Games played:

Something disappointing:

Next time I'll do this differently:

Alafia River State Park
City: Lithia   County: Hillsborough

Plan your Trip https://www.floridastateparks.org/Alafia

Activities:

- ❑ Beach Access
- ❑ Biking Trails
- ❑ Boating
- ❑ Campfire
- ❑ Caving
- ❑ Disc Golf
- ❑ Fishing
- ❑ Geo Cache
- ❑ Golf
- ❑ Hiking
- ❑ Horseback

- ❑ Hunting
- ❑ OHV
- ❑ Park Tours
- ❑ Rock Climbing
- ❑ Snorkeling
- ❑ Stargazing
- ❑ Swimming
- ❑ Viewpoint
- ❑ Wildlife & Birding
- ❑
- ❑

Facilities:

- ❑ ADA
- ❑ Gym
- ❑ Historic Sites
- ❑ Lodge
- ❑ Meeting Hall
- ❑ Pavilions
- ❑ Picnic sites
- ❑ Pool
- ❑ Restrooms

- ❑ Showers
- ❑ Visitor Center
- ❑ RV Camp
- ❑ Tent Camp
- ❑ Cabins
- ❑ Lodge Rooms
- ❑
- ❑
- ❑

Notes:

Get the Facts

- ❑ Phone: 813-672-5320
- ❑ Park Hours

  _____

- ❑ Reservations? ____Y ____N

  date made_____

- ❑ Open year 'round ___Y___N

  dates_____

- ❑ Check in time _____
- ❑ Check out time _____
- ❑ Dog friendly _____Y _____N
- ❑ Max RV length _____
- ❑ Distance from home

  miles: _____

  hours: _____

- ❑ Address_____

  _____

  _____

Fees:

- ❑ Day Use $ _____
- ❑ Camp Sites $_____
- ❑ RV Sites $ _____
- ❑ Refund policy

  _____

  _____

  _____

Make It Personal

Trip dates: _____

Why I went: _____

I went with: _____

How I got there: (circle all that apply) Plane   Train   Car   Bus   Bike   Hike   RV   MC

We stayed in (space, cabin, etc.) _____

_____

The weather was: Sunny   Cloudy   Rainy   Stormy   Snowy   Foggy   Warm   Cold

Most relaxing day: _____

_____

_____

Something funny: _____

_____

_____

Someone we met: _____

_____

_____

Best story told: _____

_____

_____

The kids liked this: _____

The best food: _____

_____

Games played: _____

_____

Something disappointing: _____

_____

Next time I'll do this differently: _____

_____

Hillsborough River State Park
City: Thonotosassa   County: Hillsborough

Plan your Trip https://www.floridastateparks.org/parks-and-trails/hillsborough-river-state-park

Activities:

- ❑ Beach Access
- ❑ Biking Trails
- ❑ Boating
- ❑ Campfire
- ❑ Caving
- ❑ Disc Golf
- ❑ Fishing
- ❑ Geo Cache
- ❑ Golf
- ❑ Hiking
- ❑ Horseback

- ❑ Hunting
- ❑ OHV
- ❑ Park Tours
- ❑ Rock Climbing
- ❑ Snorkeling
- ❑ Stargazing
- ❑ Swimming
- ❑ Viewpoint
- ❑ Wildlife & Birding
- ❑
- ❑

Facilities:

- ❑ ADA
- ❑ Gym
- ❑ Historic Sites
- ❑ Lodge
- ❑ Meeting Hall
- ❑ Pavilions
- ❑ Picnic sites
- ❑ Pool
- ❑ Restrooms

- ❑ Showers
- ❑ Visitor Center
- ❑ RV Camp
- ❑ Tent Camp
- ❑ Cabins
- ❑ Lodge Rooms
- ❑
- ❑
- ❑

Notes:

Get the Facts

- ❑ Phone: 813-987-6771 or
       941-256-6689
- ❑ Park Hours
  _____
- ❑ Reservations? ____Y ____N
  date made_____
- ❑ Open year 'round ___Y___N
  dates_____
- ❑ Check in time _____
- ❑ Check out time _____
- ❑ Dog friendly _____Y _____N
- ❑ Max RV length _____
- ❑ Distance from home
  miles: _____
  hours: _____
- ❑ Address_____
  _____

Fees:

- ❑ Day Use $ _____
- ❑ Camp Sites $_____
- ❑ RV Sites $ _____
- ❑ Refund policy
  _____
  _____
  _____

Make It Personal

Trip dates:

Why I went:

I went with:

How I got there: (circle all that apply) Plane   Train   Car   Bus   Bike   Hike   RV   MC

We stayed in (space, cabin, etc.)

The weather was: Sunny   Cloudy   Rainy   Stormy   Snowy   Foggy   Warm   Cold

Most relaxing day:

Something funny:

Someone we met:

Best story told:

The kids liked this:

The best food:

Games played:

Something disappointing:

Next time I'll do this differently:

Little Manatee River State Park
City: Wimauma   County: Hillsborough

Plan your Trip https://www.floridastateparks.org/parks-and-trails/little-manatee-river-state-park

Activities:

- ❑ Beach Access
- ❑ Biking Trails
- ❑ Boating
- ❑ Campfire
- ❑ Caving
- ❑ Disc Golf
- ❑ Fishing
- ❑ Geo Cache
- ❑ Golf
- ❑ Hiking
- ❑ Horseback

- ❑ Hunting
- ❑ OHV
- ❑ Park Tours
- ❑ Rock Climbing
- ❑ Snorkeling
- ❑ Stargazing
- ❑ Swimming
- ❑ Viewpoint
- ❑ Wildlife & Birding
- ❑
- ❑

Facilities:

- ❑ ADA
- ❑ Gym
- ❑ Historic Sites
- ❑ Lodge
- ❑ Meeting Hall
- ❑ Pavilions
- ❑ Picnic sites
- ❑ Pool
- ❑ Restrooms

- ❑ Showers
- ❑ Visitor Center
- ❑ RV Camp
- ❑ Tent Camp
- ❑ Cabins
- ❑ Lodge Rooms
- ❑
- ❑
- ❑

Notes:

Get the Facts

- ❑ Phone: 813-671-5005
- ❑ Park Hours

    _____

- ❑ Reservations? ____Y ____N

    date made_____

- ❑ Open year 'round ___Y___N

    dates_____

- ❑ Check in time _____
- ❑ Check out time _____
- ❑ Dog friendly _____Y _____N
- ❑ Max RV length _____
- ❑ Distance from home

    miles: _____

    hours: _____

- ❑ Address_____

    _____

    _____

Fees:

- ❑ Day Use $ _____
- ❑ Camp Sites $_____
- ❑ RV Sites $ _____
- ❑ Refund policy

    _____

    _____

    _____

Make It Personal

Trip dates: _____

Why I went: _____

I went with: _____

How I got there: (circle all that apply) Plane Train Car Bus Bike Hike RV MC

We stayed in (space, cabin, etc.) _____

The weather was: Sunny Cloudy Rainy Stormy Snowy Foggy Warm Cold

Most relaxing day: _____

_____

Something funny: _____

_____

Someone we met: _____

_____

Best story told: _____

_____

The kids liked this: _____

The best food: _____

Games played: _____

Something disappointing: _____

Next time I'll do this differently: _____

Lake Manatee State Park

City: Bradenton   County: Manatee

Plan your Trip https://www.floridastateparks.org/parks-and-trails/lake-manatee-state-park

Activities:

- ❑ Beach Access
- ❑ Biking Trails
- ❑ Boating
- ❑ Campfire
- ❑ Caving
- ❑ Disc Golf
- ❑ Fishing
- ❑ Geo Cache
- ❑ Golf
- ❑ Hiking
- ❑ Horseback
- ❑ Hunting
- ❑ OHV
- ❑ Park Tours
- ❑ Rock Climbing
- ❑ Snorkeling
- ❑ Stargazing
- ❑ Swimming
- ❑ Viewpoint
- ❑ Wildlife & Birding
- ❑
- ❑

Facilities:

- ❑ ADA
- ❑ Gym
- ❑ Historic Sites
- ❑ Lodge
- ❑ Meeting Hall
- ❑ Pavilions
- ❑ Picnic sites
- ❑ Pool
- ❑ Restrooms
- ❑ Showers
- ❑ Visitor Center
- ❑ RV Camp
- ❑ Tent Camp
- ❑ Cabins
- ❑ Lodge Rooms
- ❑
- ❑
- ❑

Notes:

Get the Facts

- ❑ Phone: 941-741-3028
- ❑ Park Hours

_____

- ❑ Reservations? ____Y ____N

date made_____

- ❑ Open year 'round ___Y___N

dates_____

- ❑ Check in time _____
- ❑ Check out time _____
- ❑ Dog friendly _____Y _____N
- ❑ Max RV length _____
- ❑ Distance from home

miles: _____

hours: _____

- ❑ Address_____

_____

_____

Fees:

- ❑ Day Use $ _____
- ❑ Camp Sites $_____
- ❑ RV Sites $ _____
- ❑ Refund policy

_____

_____

_____

Make It Personal

Trip dates: _____

Why I went: _____

I went with: _____

How I got there: (circle all that apply) Plane   Train   Car   Bus   Bike   Hike   RV   MC

We stayed in (space, cabin, etc.) _____

The weather was: Sunny   Cloudy   Rainy   Stormy   Snowy   Foggy   Warm   Cold

Most relaxing day: _____

Something funny: _____

Someone we met: _____

Best story told: _____

The kids liked this: _____

The best food: _____

Games played: _____

Something disappointing: _____

Next time I'll do this differently: _____

Caladesi Island State Park
City: Dunedin   County: Pinellas

Plan your Trip https://www.floridastateparks.org/parks-and-trails/caladesi-island-state-park

Activities:

- ❏ Beach Access
- ❏ Biking Trails
- ❏ Boating
- ❏ Campfire
- ❏ Caving
- ❏ Disc Golf
- ❏ Fishing
- ❏ Geo Cache
- ❏ Golf
- ❏ Hiking
- ❏ Horseback

- ❏ Hunting
- ❏ OHV
- ❏ Park Tours
- ❏ Rock Climbing
- ❏ Snorkeling
- ❏ Stargazing
- ❏ Swimming
- ❏ Viewpoint
- ❏ Wildlife & Birding
- ❏
- ❏

Facilities:

- ❏ ADA
- ❏ Gym
- ❏ Historic Sites
- ❏ Lodge
- ❏ Meeting Hall
- ❏ Pavilions
- ❏ Picnic sites
- ❏ Pool
- ❏ Restrooms

- ❏ Showers
- ❏ Visitor Center
- ❏ RV Camp
- ❏ Tent Camp
- ❏ Cabins
- ❏ Lodge Rooms
- ❏
- ❏
- ❏

Notes:

Get the Facts

- ❏ Phone: 727-469-5918
- ❏ Park Hours

  _____

- ❏ Reservations? ____Y ____N

  date made_____

- ❏ Open year 'round ___Y___N

  dates_____

- ❏ Check in time _____
- ❏ Check out time _____
- ❏ Dog friendly _____Y _____N
- ❏ Max RV length _____
- ❏ Distance from home

  miles: _____

  hours: _____

- ❏ Address_____

  _____

  _____

Fees:

- ❏ Day Use $ _____
- ❏ Camp Sites $_____
- ❏ RV Sites $ _____
- ❏ Refund policy

  _____

  _____

  _____

Make It Personal

Trip dates:

Why I went:

I went with:

How I got there: (circle all that apply) Plane   Train   Car   Bus   Bike   Hike   RV   MC

We stayed in (space, cabin, etc.)

The weather was: Sunny   Cloudy   Rainy   Stormy   Snowy   Foggy   Warm   Cold

Most relaxing day:

Something funny:

Someone we met:

Best story told:

The kids liked this:

The best food:

Games played:

Something disappointing:

Next time I'll do this differently:

Anclote Key Preserve State Park
City: Tarpon Springs   County: Pinellas

Plan your Trip https://www.floridastateparks.org/parks-and-trails/anclote-key-preserve-state-park

Activities:

- ❑ Beach Access
- ❑ Biking Trails
- ❑ Boating
- ❑ Campfire
- ❑ Caving
- ❑ Disc Golf
- ❑ Fishing
- ❑ Geo Cache
- ❑ Golf
- ❑ Hiking
- ❑ Horseback

- ❑ Hunting
- ❑ OHV
- ❑ Park Tours
- ❑ Rock Climbing
- ❑ Snorkeling
- ❑ Stargazing
- ❑ Swimming
- ❑ Viewpoint
- ❑ Wildlife & Birding
- ❑
- ❑

Facilities:

- ❑ ADA
- ❑ Gym
- ❑ Historic Sites
- ❑ Lodge
- ❑ Meeting Hall
- ❑ Pavilions
- ❑ Picnic sites
- ❑ Pool
- ❑ Restrooms

- ❑ Showers
- ❑ Visitor Center
- ❑ RV Camp
- ❑ Tent Camp
- ❑ Cabins
- ❑ Lodge Rooms
- ❑
- ❑
- ❑

Notes:

Get the Facts

- ❑ Phone: 727-241-6106
- ❑ Park Hours

  _____

- ❑ Reservations? ____Y ____N

  date made_____

- ❑ Open year 'round ___Y___N

  dates_____

- ❑ Check in time _____
- ❑ Check out time _____
- ❑ Dog friendly _____Y _____N
- ❑ Max RV length _____
- ❑ Distance from home

  miles: _____

  hours: _____

- ❑ Address_____

  _____

  _____

Fees:

- ❑ Day Use $ _____
- ❑ Camp Sites $_____
- ❑ RV Sites $ _____
- ❑ Refund policy

  _____

  _____

  _____

Make It Personal

Trip dates:
_____

Why I went:
_____

I went with:
_____

How I got there: (circle all that apply) Plane   Train   Car   Bus   Bike   Hike   RV   MC

We stayed in (space, cabin, etc.)
_____

The weather was: Sunny   Cloudy   Rainy   Stormy   Snowy   Foggy   Warm   Cold

Most relaxing day:
_____
_____

Something funny:
_____
_____

Someone we met:
_____
_____

Best story told:
_____
_____

The kids liked this:
_____

The best food:
_____

Games played:
_____
_____

Something disappointing:
_____
_____

Next time I'll do this differently:
_____
_____

Oscar Scherer State Park
City: Osprey   County: Sarasota

Plan your Trip https://www.floridastateparks.org/parks-and-trails/oscar-scherer-state-park

Activities:

- ❏ Beach Access
- ❏ Biking Trails
- ❏ Boating
- ❏ Campfire
- ❏ Caving
- ❏ Disc Golf
- ❏ Fishing
- ❏ Geo Cache
- ❏ Golf
- ❏ Hiking
- ❏ Horseback

- ❏ Hunting
- ❏ OHV
- ❏ Park Tours
- ❏ Rock Climbing
- ❏ Snorkeling
- ❏ Stargazing
- ❏ Swimming
- ❏ Viewpoint
- ❏ Wildlife & Birding
- ❏
- ❏

Facilities:

- ❏ ADA
- ❏ Gym
- ❏ Historic Sites
- ❏ Lodge
- ❏ Meeting Hall
- ❏ Pavilions
- ❏ Picnic sites
- ❏ Pool
- ❏ Restrooms

- ❏ Showers
- ❏ Visitor Center
- ❏ RV Camp
- ❏ Tent Camp
- ❏ Cabins
- ❏ Lodge Rooms
- ❏
- ❏
- ❏

Notes:

Get the Facts

- ❏ Phone: 941-483-5956
- ❏ Park Hours

  _____

- ❏ Reservations? ____Y ____N

  date made_____

- ❏ Open year 'round ___Y___N

  dates_____

- ❏ Check in time _____

- ❏ Check out time _____

- ❏ Dog friendly _____Y _____N

- ❏ Max RV length _____

- ❏ Distance from home

  miles: _____

  hours: _____

- ❏ Address_____

  _____

  _____

Fees:

- ❏ Day Use $ _____
- ❏ Camp Sites $_____
- ❏ RV Sites $ _____
- ❏ Refund policy

  _____

  _____

  _____

Make It Personal

Trip dates: _____

Why I went: _____

I went with: _____

How I got there: (circle all that apply) Plane   Train   Car   Bus   Bike   Hike   RV   MC

We stayed in (space, cabin, etc.) _____

The weather was: Sunny   Cloudy   Rainy   Stormy   Snowy   Foggy   Warm   Cold

Most relaxing day: _____

_____

Something funny: _____

_____

Someone we met: _____

_____

Best story told: _____

_____

The kids liked this: _____

The best food: _____

_____

Games played: _____

Something disappointing: _____

Next time I'll do this differently: _____

Myakka River State Park
City: Sarasota   County: Sarasota

Plan your Trip https://www.floridastateparks.org/parks-and-trails/myakka-river-state-park

Activities:

- ❑ Beach Access
- ❑ Biking Trails
- ❑ Boating
- ❑ Campfire
- ❑ Caving
- ❑ Disc Golf
- ❑ Fishing
- ❑ Geo Cache
- ❑ Golf
- ❑ Hiking
- ❑ Horseback

- ❑ Hunting
- ❑ OHV
- ❑ Park Tours
- ❑ Rock Climbing
- ❑ Snorkeling
- ❑ Stargazing
- ❑ Swimming
- ❑ Viewpoint
- ❑ Wildlife & Birding
- ❑
- ❑

Facilities:

- ❑ ADA
- ❑ Gym
- ❑ Historic Sites
- ❑ Lodge
- ❑ Meeting Hall
- ❑ Pavilions
- ❑ Picnic sites
- ❑ Pool
- ❑ Restrooms

- ❑ Showers
- ❑ Visitor Center
- ❑ RV Camp
- ❑ Tent Camp
- ❑ Cabins
- ❑ Lodge Rooms
- ❑
- ❑
- ❑

Notes:

Get the Facts

- ❑ Phone: 941-361-6511
- ❑ Park Hours

  _____

- ❑ Reservations? ____Y ____N

  date made_____

- ❑ Open year 'round ___Y___N

  dates_____

- ❑ Check in time _____
- ❑ Check out time _____
- ❑ Dog friendly _____Y _____N
- ❑ Max RV length _____
- ❑ Distance from home

  miles: _____

  hours: _____

- ❑ Address_____

  _____

  _____

Fees:

- ❑ Day Use $ _____
- ❑ Camp Sites $_____
- ❑ RV Sites $ _____
- ❑ Refund policy

  _____

  _____

  _____

Make It Personal

Trip dates: _____

Why I went: _____

I went with: _____

How I got there: (circle all that apply) Plane   Train   Car   Bus   Bike   Hike   RV   MC

We stayed in (space, cabin, etc.)
_____

The weather was: Sunny   Cloudy   Rainy   Stormy   Snowy   Foggy   Warm   Cold

Most relaxing day:
_____

Something funny:
_____

Someone we met:
_____

Best story told:
_____

The kids liked this: _____

The best food: _____

Games played: _____

Something disappointing: _____

Next time I'll do this differently: _____

Crystal River Archaeological State Park
City: Crystal River   County: Citrus

Plan your trip https://www.floridastateparks.org/parks-and-trails/crystal-river-archaeological-state-park

Activities:

- ❏ Birding / Wildlife
- ❏ Fishing
- ❏ Guided tours
- ❏ Geo cache
- ❏ Hiking
- ❏ Horseback
- ❏ Hunting
- ❏ Snorkeling
- ❏ Trails
- ❏ Water access

Facilities:

- ❏ ADA
- ❏ Meeting hall
- ❏ Pavilions
- ❏ Picnic sites
- ❏ Restrooms
- ❏ Visitor center
- ❏
- ❏
- ❏
- ❏

Get the Facts

- ❏ Phone 352-795-3817
- ❏ Park Hours

  _____

- ❏ Reservations? ____Y ____N

  date made_____

- ❏ Open year 'round ___Y___N

  dates_____

- ❏ Distance from home

  miles: _____

  hours: _____

- ❏ Address or GPS

  _____

  _____

Date visited:

I went with:
_____

My favorite things:
_____

_____

_____

Notes

Fees:

- ❏ Day Use $ _____
- ❏ Parking $_____
- ❏ Refund policy

  _____

  _____

Crystal River Preserve State Park
City: Crystal River   County: Citrus

Plan your trip https://www.floridastateparks.org/parks-and-trails/crystal-river-preserve-state-park

Activities:

- ❑ Birding / Wildlife
- ❑ Fishing
- ❑ Guided tours
- ❑ Geo cache
- ❑ Hiking
- ❑ Horseback
- ❑ Hunting
- ❑ Snorkeling
- ❑ Trails
- ❑ Water access

Facilities:

- ❑ ADA
- ❑ Meeting hall
- ❑ Pavilions
- ❑ Picnic sites
- ❑ Restrooms
- ❑ Visitor center
- ❑
- ❑
- ❑
- ❑

Get the Facts

- ❑ Phone 352-228-6028
- ❑ Park Hours

  _____

- ❑ Reservations? ____Y ____N

  date made_____

- ❑ Open year 'round ___Y___N

  dates_____

- ❑ Distance from home

  miles: _____

  hours: _____

- ❑ Address or GPS

  _____

  _____

Date visited:

I went with:

_____

My favorite things:

_____

_____

_____

Notes

Fees:

- ❑ Day Use $ _____
- ❑ Parking $_____
- ❑ Refund policy

  _____

  _____

Felburn Park
City: Crystal River   County: Citrus

Plan your trip https://www.floridastateparks.org/parks-and-trails/felburn-park

Activities:

- ❑ Birding / Wildlife
- ❑ Fishing
- ❑ Guided tours
- ❑ Geo cache
- ❑ Hiking
- ❑ Horseback
- ❑ Hunting
- ❑ Snorkeling
- ❑ Trails
- ❑ Water access

Facilities:

- ❑ ADA
- ❑ Meeting hall
- ❑ Pavilions
- ❑ Picnic sites
- ❑ Restrooms
- ❑ Visitor center
- ❑
- ❑
- ❑
- ❑

Get the Facts

- ❑ Phone 352-236-7143
- ❑ Park Hours

  _____

- ❑ Reservations? ____Y ____N

  date made_____

- ❑ Open year 'round ___Y___N

  dates_____

- ❑ Distance from home

  miles: _____

  hours: _____

- ❑ Address or GPS

  _____

  _____

Date visited:

I went with:
_____

My favorite things:
_____
_____
_____

Notes

Fees:

- ❑ Day Use $ _____
- ❑ Parking $_____
- ❑ Refund policy

  _____

  _____

Inglis Dam & Island Recreation Area
City: Crystal River   County: Citrus

Plan your trip https://www.floridastateparks.org/parks-and-trails/inglis-dam-island-recreation-area

Activities:

❑ Birding / Wildlife
❑ Fishing
❑ Guided tours
❑ Geo cache
❑ Hiking
❑ Horseback
❑ Hunting
❑ Snorkeling
❑ Trails
❑ Water access

Facilities:

❑ ADA
❑ Meeting hall
❑ Pavilions
❑ Picnic sites
❑ Restrooms
❑ Visitor center
❑
❑
❑
❑

Get the Facts

❑ Phone 352-236-7143
❑ Park Hours

_____

❑ Reservations? ____Y ____N

date made_____

❑ Open year 'round ___Y___N

dates_____

❑ Distance from home

miles: _____

hours: _____

❑ Address or GPS

_____

_____

Date visited:

I went with:
_____

My favorite things:
_____

_____

_____

Notes

Fees:

❑ Day Use $ _____
❑ Parking $_____
❑ Refund policy

_____

_____

Ellie Schiller Homosassa Springs Wildlife State Park

City: Homosassa   County: Citrus

Plan your trip https://www.floridastateparks.org/parks-and-trails/ellie-schiller-homosassa-springs-wildlife-state-park

Activities:

- ❑ Birding / Wildlife
- ❑ Fishing
- ❑ Guided tours
- ❑ Geo cache
- ❑ Hiking
- ❑ Horseback
- ❑ Hunting
- ❑ Snorkeling
- ❑ Trails
- ❑ Water access

Facilities:

- ❑ ADA
- ❑ Meeting hall
- ❑ Pavilions
- ❑ Picnic sites
- ❑ Restrooms
- ❑ Visitor center
- ❑
- ❑
- ❑
- ❑

Get the Facts

- ❑ Phone 352-628-5343
- ❑ Park Hours

  _____

- ❑ Reservations? ____Y ____N

  date made_____

- ❑ Open year 'round ___Y___N

  dates_____

- ❑ Distance from home

  miles: _____

  hours: _____

- ❑ Address or GPS

  _____

  _____

Date visited:

I went with:
_____

My favorite things:
_____

_____

_____

Notes

Fees:

- ❑ Day Use $ _____
- ❑ Parking $_____
- ❑ Refund policy

  _____

  _____

Yulee Sugar Mill Ruins Historic SP
City: Homosassa   County: Citrus

Plan your trip https://www.floridastateparks.org/parks-and-trails/yulee-sugar-mill-ruins-historic-state-park

Activities:

- ❑ Birding / Wildlife
- ❑ Fishing
- ❑ Guided tours
- ❑ Geo cache
- ❑ Hiking
- ❑ Horseback
- ❑ Hunting
- ❑ Snorkeling
- ❑ Trails
- ❑ Water access

Facilities:

- ❑ ADA
- ❑ Meeting hall
- ❑ Pavilions
- ❑ Picnic sites
- ❑ Restrooms
- ❑ Visitor center
- ❑
- ❑
- ❑
- ❑

Get the Facts

- ❑ Phone 352-795-3817
- ❑ Park Hours

    _____

- ❑ Reservations? ____Y ____N

    date made_____

- ❑ Open year 'round ___Y___N

    dates_____

- ❑ Distance from home

    miles: _____

    hours: _____

- ❑ Address or GPS

    _____

    _____

Date visited:

I went with:
_____

My favorite things:
_____

_____

_____

Fees:

- ❑ Day Use $ _____
- ❑ Parking $_____
- ❑ Refund policy

    _____

    _____

Notes

Weeki Wachee Springs State Park
City: Weeki Wachee   County: Hernando

Plan your trip https://www.floridastateparks.org/index.php/WeekiWachee

Activities:

- ❑ Birding / Wildlife
- ❑ Fishing
- ❑ Guided tours
- ❑ Geo cache
- ❑ Hiking
- ❑ Horseback
- ❑ Hunting
- ❑ Snorkeling
- ❑ Trails
- ❑ Water access

Facilities:

- ❑ ADA
- ❑ Meeting hall
- ❑ Pavilions
- ❑ Picnic sites
- ❑ Restrooms
- ❑ Visitor center
- ❑
- ❑
- ❑
- ❑

Get the Facts

- ❑ Phone 352-592-5656
- ❑ Park Hours

_____

- ❑ Reservations? ____Y ____N

date made_____

- ❑ Open year 'round ___Y___N

dates_____

- ❑ Distance from home

miles: _____

hours: _____

- ❑ Address or GPS

_____

_____

Date visited:

I went with:
_____

My favorite things:
_____

_____

_____

Notes

Fees:

- ❑ Day Use $ _____
- ❑ Parking $_____
- ❑ Refund policy

_____

_____

Cockroach Bay Preserve State Park

City: Ruskin   County: Hillsborough

Plan your trip https://www.floridastateparks.org/parks-and-trails/cockroach-bay-preserve-state-park

Activities:

- ❑ Birding / Wildlife
- ❑ Fishing
- ❑ Guided tours
- ❑ Geo cache
- ❑ Hiking
- ❑ Horseback
- ❑ Hunting
- ❑ Snorkeling
- ❑ Trails
- ❑ Water access

Facilities:

- ❑ ADA
- ❑ Meeting hall
- ❑ Pavilions
- ❑ Picnic sites
- ❑ Restrooms
- ❑ Visitor center
- ❑
- ❑
- ❑
- ❑

Get the Facts

- ❑ Phone 941-723-4536
- ❑ Park Hours

  _____

- ❑ Reservations? ____Y ____N

  date made_____

- ❑ Open year 'round ___Y___N

  dates_____

- ❑ Distance from home

  miles: _____

  hours: _____

- ❑ Address or GPS

  _____

  _____

Date visited:

I went with:

_____

My favorite things:

_____

_____

_____

Notes

Fees:

- ❑ Day Use $ _____
- ❑ Parking $_____
- ❑ Refund policy

  _____

  _____

Ybor City Museum State Park

City: Tamps   County: Hillsborough

Plan your trip https://www.floridastateparks.org/parks-and-trails/ybor-city-museum-state-park

Activities:

- ❑ Birding / Wildlife
- ❑ Fishing
- ❑ Guided tours
- ❑ Geo cache
- ❑ Hiking
- ❑ Horseback
- ❑ Hunting
- ❑ Snorkeling
- ❑ Trails
- ❑ Water access

Facilities:

- ❑ ADA
- ❑ Meeting hall
- ❑ Pavilions
- ❑ Picnic sites
- ❑ Restrooms
- ❑ Visitor center
- ❑
- ❑
- ❑
- ❑

Get the Facts

- ❑ Phone 813-247-6323
- ❑ Park Hours

  _____
- ❑ Reservations? ____Y ____N

  date made_____
- ❑ Open year 'round ___Y___N

  dates_____
- ❑ Distance from home

  miles: _____

  hours: _____
- ❑ Address or GPS

  _____

  _____

Date visited:

I went with:
_____

My favorite things:
_____

_____

_____

Notes

Fees:

- ❑ Day Use $ _____
- ❑ Parking $_____
- ❑ Refund policy

  _____

  _____

156

Fort Foster State Historic Site
City: Thonotosassa   County: Hillsborough

Plan your trip https://www.floridastateparks.org/index.php/parks-and-trails/fort-foster-state-historic-site

Activities:

- ❑ Birding / Wildlife
- ❑ Fishing
- ❑ Guided tours
- ❑ Geo cache
- ❑ Hiking
- ❑ Horseback
- ❑ Hunting
- ❑ Snorkeling
- ❑ Trails
- ❑ Water access

Facilities:

- ❑ ADA
- ❑ Meeting hall
- ❑ Pavilions
- ❑ Picnic sites
- ❑ Restrooms
- ❑ Visitor center
- ❑
- ❑
- ❑
- ❑

Get the Facts

- ❑ Phone 813-987-6771
- ❑ Park Hours

  _____

- ❑ Reservations? ____Y ____N

  date made_____

- ❑ Open year 'round ___Y___N

  dates_____

- ❑ Distance from home

  miles: _____

  hours: _____

- ❑ Address or GPS

  _____

  _____

Date visited:

I went with:
_____

My favorite things:
_____

_____

_____

Notes

Fees:

- ❑ Day Use $ _____
- ❑ Parking $_____
- ❑ Refund policy

  _____

  _____

Judah P. Benjamin Confederate Memorial at Gamble Plantation HSP

City: Ellenton   County: Manatee

Plan your trip https://www.floridastateparks.org/index.php/parks-and-trails/judah-p-benjamin-confederate-memorial-gamble-plantation-historic-state-park

Activities:

- ❏ Birding / Wildlife
- ❏ Fishing
- ❏ Guided tours
- ❏ Geo cache
- ❏ Hiking
- ❏ Horseback
- ❏ Hunting
- ❏ Snorkeling
- ❏ Trails
- ❏ Water access

Facilities:

- ❏ ADA
- ❏ Meeting hall
- ❏ Pavilions
- ❏ Picnic sites
- ❏ Restrooms
- ❏ Visitor center
- ❏
- ❏
- ❏
- ❏

Get the Facts

- ❏ Phone 941-723-4536
- ❏ Park Hours

  _____

- ❏ Reservations? ____Y ____N

  date made_____

- ❏ Open year 'round ___Y___N

  dates_____

- ❏ Distance from home

  miles: _____

  hours: _____

- ❏ Address or GPS

  _____

  _____

Date visited:

I went with:
_____

My favorite things:
_____
_____
_____

Notes

Fees:

- ❏ Day Use $ _____
- ❏ Parking $_____
- ❏ Refund policy

  _____

  _____

Madira Bickel Mound State Archeological Site

City: Tera Ceia   County: Manatee

Plan your trip https://www.floridastateparks.org/index.php/parks-and-trails/madira-bickel-mound-state-archaeological-site

Activities:

- ❑ Birding / Wildlife
- ❑ Fishing
- ❑ Guided tours
- ❑ Geo cache
- ❑ Hiking
- ❑ Horseback
- ❑ Hunting
- ❑ Snorkeling
- ❑ Trails
- ❑ Water access

Facilities:

- ❑ ADA
- ❑ Meeting hall
- ❑ Pavilions
- ❑ Picnic sites
- ❑ Restrooms
- ❑ Visitor center
- ❑
- ❑
- ❑
- ❑

Get the Facts

- ❑ Phone 941-723-4536
- ❑ Park Hours

_____

- ❑ Reservations? ____Y ____N

date made_____

- ❑ Open year 'round ___Y___N

dates_____

- ❑ Distance from home

miles: _____

hours: _____

- ❑ Address or GPS

_____

_____

Date visited:

I went with:

_____

My favorite things:

_____

_____

_____

Notes

Fees:

- ❑ Day Use $ _____
- ❑ Parking $_____
- ❑ Refund policy

_____

_____

Terra Ceia Preserve State Park
City: Terra Ceia   County: Manatee

Plan your trip https://www.floridastateparks.org/parks-and-trails/terra-ceia-preserve-state-park

Activities:

- ❑ Birding / Wildlife
- ❑ Fishing
- ❑ Guided tours
- ❑ Geo cache
- ❑ Hiking
- ❑ Horseback
- ❑ Hunting
- ❑ Snorkeling
- ❑ Trails
- ❑ Water access

Facilities:

- ❑ ADA
- ❑ Meeting hall
- ❑ Pavilions
- ❑ Picnic sites
- ❑ Restrooms
- ❑ Visitor center
- ❑
- ❑
- ❑
- ❑

Get the Facts

- ❑ Phone 941-723-4536
- ❑ Park Hours

  _____

- ❑ Reservations? ____Y ____N

  date made_____

- ❑ Open year 'round ___Y___N

  dates_____

- ❑ Distance from home

  miles: _____

  hours: _____

- ❑ Address or GPS

  _____

  _____

Date visited:

I went with:
_____

My favorite things:
_____

_____

_____

Fees:

- ❑ Day Use $ _____
- ❑ Parking $_____
- ❑ Refund policy

  _____

  _____

Notes

Werner-Boyce Salt Springs SP
City: Port Richey　　　　　County: Pasco

Plan your trip https://www.floridastateparks.org/parks-and-trails/werner-boyce-salt-springs-state-park

Activities:

- ❏ Birding / Wildlife
- ❏ Fishing
- ❏ Guided tours
- ❏ Geo cache
- ❏ Hiking
- ❏ Horseback
- ❏ Hunting
- ❏ Snorkeling
- ❏ Trails
- ❏ Water access

Facilities:

- ❏ ADA
- ❏ Meeting hall
- ❏ Pavilions
- ❏ Picnic sites
- ❏ Restrooms
- ❏ Visitor center
- ❏
- ❏
- ❏
- ❏

Get the Facts

- ❏ Phone 727-816-1890
- ❏ Park Hours

  _____

- ❏ Reservations? ____Y ____N

  date made_____

- ❏ Open year 'round ___Y___N

  dates_____

- ❏ Distance from home

  miles: _____

  hours: _____

- ❏ Address or GPS

  _____

  _____

Date visited:

I went with:
_____

My favorite things:
_____
_____
_____

Notes

Fees:

- ❏ Day Use $ _____
- ❏ Parking $_____
- ❏ Refund policy

  _____

  _____

Honeymoon Island State Park

City: Dunedin   **County: Pinellas**

Plan your trip https://www.floridastateparks.org/index.php/honeymoonisland

Activities:

- ❏ Birding / Wildlife
- ❏ Fishing
- ❏ Guided tours
- ❏ Geo cache
- ❏ Hiking
- ❏ Horseback
- ❏ Hunting
- ❏ Snorkeling
- ❏ Trails
- ❏ Water access

Facilities:

- ❏ ADA
- ❏ Meeting hall
- ❏ Pavilions
- ❏ Picnic sites
- ❏ Restrooms
- ❏ Visitor center
- ❏
- ❏
- ❏
- ❏

Get the Facts

- ❏ Phone 727-241-6106
- ❏ Park Hours

_____

- ❏ Reservations? ____Y ____N

date made_____

- ❏ Open year 'round ___Y___N

dates_____

- ❏ Distance from home

miles: _____

hours: _____

- ❏ Address or GPS

_____

_____

Date visited:

I went with:
_____

My favorite things:
_____

_____

_____

Notes

Fees:

- ❏ Day Use $ _____
- ❏ Parking $_____
- ❏ Refund policy

_____

_____

Egmont Key State Park
City: St. Petersburg   County: Pinellas

Plan your trip https://www.floridastateparks.org/parks-and-trails/egmont-key-state-park

Activities:

- ❑ Birding / Wildlife
- ❑ Fishing
- ❑ Guided tours
- ❑ Geo cache
- ❑ Hiking
- ❑ Horseback
- ❑ Hunting
- ❑ Snorkeling
- ❑ Trails
- ❑ Water access

Facilities:

- ❑ ADA
- ❑ Meeting hall
- ❑ Pavilions
- ❑ Picnic sites
- ❑ Restrooms
- ❑ Visitor center
- ❑
- ❑
- ❑
- ❑

Get the Facts

- ❑ Phone 727-644-6235
- ❑ Park Hours

  _____

- ❑ Reservations? ____Y ____N

  date made_____

- ❑ Open year 'round ___Y___N

  dates_____

- ❑ Distance from home

  miles: _____

  hours: _____

- ❑ Address or GPS

  _____

  _____

Date visited:

I went with:
_____

My favorite things:
_____

_____

_____

Notes

Fees:

- ❑ Day Use $ _____
- ❑ Parking $_____
- ❑ Refund policy

  _____

  _____

Skyway Fishing Pier State Park
City: St. Petersburg   County: Pinellas

Plan your trip https://www.floridastateparks.org/index.php/parks-and-trails/skyway-fishing-pier-state-park

Activities:

- ❑ Birding / Wildlife
- ❑ Fishing
- ❑ Guided tours
- ❑ Geo cache
- ❑ Hiking
- ❑ Horseback
- ❑ Hunting
- ❑ Snorkeling
- ❑ Trails
- ❑ Water access

Facilities:

- ❑ ADA
- ❑ Meeting hall
- ❑ Pavilions
- ❑ Picnic sites
- ❑ Restrooms
- ❑ Visitor center
- ❑
- ❑
- ❑
- ❑

Get the Facts

- ❑ Phone 727-865-0668
- ❑ Park Hours

  _____

- ❑ Reservations? ____Y ____N

  date made_____

- ❑ Open year 'round ___Y___N

  dates_____

- ❑ Distance from home

  miles: _____

  hours: _____

- ❑ Address or GPS

  _____

  _____

Date visited:

I went with:

_____

My favorite things:

_____

_____

_____

Notes

Fees:

- ❑ Day Use $ _____
- ❑ Parking $_____
- ❑ Refund policy

  _____

  _____

Central

- Hardee
- Highlands
- Lake
- Marion
- Orange
- Polk
- Seminole
- Sumter

Highlands Hammock State Park
City: Sebring   County: Highlands

Plan your Trip https://www.floridastateparks.org/parks-and-trails/highlands-hammock-state-park

Activities:

- ❑ Beach Access
- ❑ Biking Trails
- ❑ Boating
- ❑ Campfire
- ❑ Caving
- ❑ Disc Golf
- ❑ Fishing
- ❑ Geo Cache
- ❑ Golf
- ❑ Hiking
- ❑ Horseback

- ❑ Hunting
- ❑ OHV
- ❑ Park Tours
- ❑ Rock Climbing
- ❑ Snorkeling
- ❑ Stargazing
- ❑ Swimming
- ❑ Viewpoint
- ❑ Wildlife & Birding
- ❑
- ❑

Facilities:

- ❑ ADA
- ❑ Gym
- ❑ Historic Sites
- ❑ Lodge
- ❑ Meeting Hall
- ❑ Pavilions
- ❑ Picnic sites
- ❑ Pool
- ❑ Restrooms

- ❑ Showers
- ❑ Visitor Center
- ❑ RV Camp
- ❑ Tent Camp
- ❑ Cabins
- ❑ Lodge Rooms
- ❑
- ❑
- ❑

Notes:

Get the Facts

- ❑ Phone: 863-386-6094
- ❑ Park Hours

_____

- ❑ Reservations? _____Y _____N

date made_____

- ❑ Open year 'round ___Y___N

dates_____

- ❑ Check in time _____
- ❑ Check out time _____
- ❑ Dog friendly _____Y _____N
- ❑ Max RV length _____
- ❑ Distance from home

miles: _____

hours: _____

- ❑ Address_____

_____

_____

Fees:

- ❑ Day Use $ _____
- ❑ Camp Sites $_____
- ❑ RV Sites $ _____
- ❑ Refund policy

_____

_____

_____

Make It Personal

Trip dates: _____

Why I went: _____

I went with: _____

How I got there: (circle all that apply) Plane   Train   Car   Bus   Bike   Hike   RV   MC

We stayed in (space, cabin, etc.) _____

_____

The weather was: Sunny   Cloudy   Rainy   Stormy   Snowy   Foggy   Warm   Cold

Most relaxing day: _____

_____

_____

Something funny: _____

_____

_____

Someone we met: _____

_____

_____

Best story told: _____

_____

_____

The kids liked this: _____

The best food: _____

_____

Games played: _____

_____

Something disappointing: _____

_____

Next time I'll do this differently: _____

_____

Lake Louisa State Park
City: Clermont   County: Lake

Plan your Trip https://www.floridastateparks.org/parks-and-trails/lake-louisa-state-park

Activities:

- ❑ Beach Access
- ❑ Biking Trails
- ❑ Boating
- ❑ Campfire
- ❑ Caving
- ❑ Disc Golf
- ❑ Fishing
- ❑ Geo Cache
- ❑ Golf
- ❑ Hiking
- ❑ Horseback

- ❑ Hunting
- ❑ OHV
- ❑ Park Tours
- ❑ Rock Climbing
- ❑ Snorkeling
- ❑ Stargazing
- ❑ Swimming
- ❑ Viewpoint
- ❑ Wildlife & Birding
- ❑
- ❑

Facilities:

- ❑ ADA
- ❑ Gym
- ❑ Historic Sites
- ❑ Lodge
- ❑ Meeting Hall
- ❑ Pavilions
- ❑ Picnic sites
- ❑ Pool
- ❑ Restrooms

- ❑ Showers
- ❑ Visitor Center
- ❑ RV Camp
- ❑ Tent Camp
- ❑ Cabins
- ❑ Lodge Rooms
- ❑
- ❑
- ❑

Notes:

Get the Facts

- ❑ Phone: 352-394-3969
- ❑ Park Hours

  _____

- ❑ Reservations? ____Y ____N

  date made_____

- ❑ Open year 'round ___Y___N

  dates_____

- ❑ Check in time _____
- ❑ Check out time _____
- ❑ Dog friendly _____Y _____N
- ❑ Max RV length _____
- ❑ Distance from home

  miles: _____

  hours: _____

- ❑ Address_____

  _____

  _____

Fees:

- ❑ Day Use $ _____
- ❑ Camp Sites $_____
- ❑ RV Sites $ _____
- ❑ Refund policy

  _____

  _____

  _____

Make It Personal

Trip dates:

Why I went:

I went with:

How I got there: (circle all that apply) Plane   Train   Car   Bus   Bike   Hike   RV   MC

We stayed in (space, cabin, etc.)

The weather was: Sunny   Cloudy   Rainy   Stormy   Snowy   Foggy   Warm   Cold

Most relaxing day:

Something funny:

Someone we met:

Best story told:

The kids liked this:

The best food:

Games played:

Something disappointing:

Next time I'll do this differently:

169

Lake Griffin State Park
City: Fruitland Park   County: Lake

Plan your Trip https://www.floridastateparks.org/parks-and-trails/lake-griffin-state-park

Activities:

- ❑ Beach Access
- ❑ Biking Trails
- ❑ Boating
- ❑ Campfire
- ❑ Caving
- ❑ Disc Golf
- ❑ Fishing
- ❑ Geo Cache
- ❑ Golf
- ❑ Hiking
- ❑ Horseback

- ❑ Hunting
- ❑ OHV
- ❑ Park Tours
- ❑ Rock Climbing
- ❑ Snorkeling
- ❑ Stargazing
- ❑ Swimming
- ❑ Viewpoint
- ❑ Wildlife & Birding
- ❑
- ❑

Facilities:

- ❑ ADA
- ❑ Gym
- ❑ Historic Sites
- ❑ Lodge
- ❑ Meeting Hall
- ❑ Pavilions
- ❑ Picnic sites
- ❑ Pool
- ❑ Restrooms

- ❑ Showers
- ❑ Visitor Center
- ❑ RV Camp
- ❑ Tent Camp
- ❑ Cabins
- ❑ Lodge Rooms
- ❑
- ❑
- ❑

Notes:

Get the Facts

- ❑ Phone: 352-360-6760
- ❑ Park Hours

  _____

- ❑ Reservations? ____Y ____N

  date made_____

- ❑ Open year 'round ___Y___N

  dates_____

- ❑ Check in time _____
- ❑ Check out time _____
- ❑ Dog friendly _____Y _____N
- ❑ Max RV length _____
- ❑ Distance from home

  miles: _____

  hours: _____

- ❑ Address_____

  _____

  _____

Fees:

- ❑ Day Use $ _____
- ❑ Camp Sites $_____
- ❑ RV Sites $ _____
- ❑ Refund policy

  _____

  _____

  _____

Make It Personal

Trip dates:

Why I went:

I went with:

How I got there: (circle all that apply) Plane   Train   Car   Bus   Bike   Hike   RV   MC

We stayed in (space, cabin, etc.)

The weather was: Sunny   Cloudy   Rainy   Stormy   Snowy   Foggy   Warm   Cold

Most relaxing day:

Something funny:

Someone we met:

Best story told:

The kids liked this:

The best food:

Games played:

Something disappointing:

Next time I'll do this differently:

Rock Springs Run State Reserve
City: Sorrento   County: Lake

Plan your Trip https://www.floridastateparks.org/parks-and-trails/rock-springs-run-state-reserve

Activities:

- ❑ Beach Access
- ❑ Biking Trails
- ❑ Boating
- ❑ Campfire
- ❑ Caving
- ❑ Disc Golf
- ❑ Fishing
- ❑ Geo Cache
- ❑ Golf
- ❑ Hiking
- ❑ Horseback

- ❑ Hunting
- ❑ OHV
- ❑ Park Tours
- ❑ Rock Climbing
- ❑ Snorkeling
- ❑ Stargazing
- ❑ Swimming
- ❑ Viewpoint
- ❑ Wildlife & Birding
- ❑
- ❑

Facilities:

- ❑ ADA
- ❑ Gym
- ❑ Historic Sites
- ❑ Lodge
- ❑ Meeting Hall
- ❑ Pavilions
- ❑ Picnic sites
- ❑ Pool
- ❑ Restrooms

- ❑ Showers
- ❑ Visitor Center
- ❑ RV Camp
- ❑ Tent Camp
- ❑ Cabins
- ❑ Lodge Rooms
- ❑
- ❑
- ❑

Notes:

Get the Facts

- ❑ Phone: 407-553-4383
- ❑ Park Hours

  _____

- ❑ Reservations? ____Y ____N

  date made_____

- ❑ Open year 'round ___Y___N

  dates_____

- ❑ Check in time _____

- ❑ Check out time _____

- ❑ Dog friendly _____Y _____N

- ❑ Max RV length _____

- ❑ Distance from home

  miles: _____

  hours: _____

- ❑ Address_____

  _____

  _____

Fees:

- ❑ Day Use $ _____
- ❑ Camp Sites $_____
- ❑ RV Sites $ _____
- ❑ Refund policy

  _____

  _____

  _____

Make It Personal

Trip dates:

Why I went:

I went with:

How I got there: (circle all that apply) Plane   Train   Car   Bus   Bike   Hike   RV   MC

We stayed in (space, cabin, etc.)

The weather was: Sunny   Cloudy   Rainy   Stormy   Snowy   Foggy   Warm   Cold

Most relaxing day:

Something funny:

Someone we met:

Best story told:

The kids liked this:

The best food:

Games played:

Something disappointing:

Next time I'll do this differently:

Rainbow Springs State Park
City: Dunnellon   County: Marion

Plan your Trip https://www.floridastateparks.org/parks-and-trails/rainbow-springs-state-park

Activities:

- [ ] Beach Access
- [ ] Biking Trails
- [ ] Boating
- [ ] Campfire
- [ ] Caving
- [ ] Disc Golf
- [ ] Fishing
- [ ] Geo Cache
- [ ] Golf
- [ ] Hiking
- [ ] Horseback

- [ ] Hunting
- [ ] OHV
- [ ] Park Tours
- [ ] Rock Climbing
- [ ] Snorkeling
- [ ] Stargazing
- [ ] Swimming
- [ ] Viewpoint
- [ ] Wildlife & Birding
- [ ]
- [ ]

Facilities:

- [ ] ADA
- [ ] Gym
- [ ] Historic Sites
- [ ] Lodge
- [ ] Meeting Hall
- [ ] Pavilions
- [ ] Picnic sites
- [ ] Pool
- [ ] Restrooms

- [ ] Showers
- [ ] Visitor Center
- [ ] RV Camp
- [ ] Tent Camp
- [ ] Cabins
- [ ] Lodge Rooms
- [ ]
- [ ]
- [ ]

Notes:

Get the Facts

- [ ] Phone: 352-465-8555
- [ ] Park Hours

  _____

- [ ] Reservations? ____Y ____N

  date made_____

- [ ] Open year 'round ___Y___N

  dates_____

- [ ] Check in time _____
- [ ] Check out time _____
- [ ] Dog friendly _____Y _____N
- [ ] Max RV length _____
- [ ] Distance from home

  miles: _____

  hours: _____

- [ ] Address_____

  _____

  _____

Fees:

- [ ] Day Use $ _____
- [ ] Camp Sites $_____
- [ ] RV Sites $ _____
- [ ] Refund policy

  _____

  _____

  _____

Make It Personal

Trip dates:

Why I went:

I went with:

How I got there: (circle all that apply) Plane   Train   Car   Bus   Bike   Hike   RV   MC

We stayed in (space, cabin, etc.)

The weather was: Sunny   Cloudy   Rainy   Stormy   Snowy   Foggy   Warm   Cold

Most relaxing day:

Something funny:

Someone we met:

Best story told:

The kids liked this:

The best food:

Games played:

Something disappointing:

Next time I'll do this differently:

Silver Springs State Park
City: Ocala   County: Marion

Plan your Trip https://www.floridastateparks.org/silversprings

Activities:

- ❑ Beach Access
- ❑ Biking Trails
- ❑ Boating
- ❑ Campfire
- ❑ Caving
- ❑ Disc Golf
- ❑ Fishing
- ❑ Geo Cache
- ❑ Golf
- ❑ Hiking
- ❑ Horseback

- ❑ Hunting
- ❑ OHV
- ❑ Park Tours
- ❑ Rock Climbing
- ❑ Snorkeling
- ❑ Stargazing
- ❑ Swimming
- ❑ Viewpoint
- ❑ Wildlife & Birding
- ❑
- ❑

Facilities:

- ❑ ADA
- ❑ Gym
- ❑ Historic Sites
- ❑ Lodge
- ❑ Meeting Hall
- ❑ Pavilions
- ❑ Picnic sites
- ❑ Pool
- ❑ Restrooms

- ❑ Showers
- ❑ Visitor Center
- ❑ RV Camp
- ❑ Tent Camp
- ❑ Cabins
- ❑ Lodge Rooms
- ❑
- ❑
- ❑

Notes:

Get the Facts

- ❑ Phone: 352-236-7148
- ❑ Park Hours

    _____

- ❑ Reservations? ____Y ____N

    date made_____

- ❑ Open year 'round ___Y___N

    dates_____

- ❑ Check in time _____
- ❑ Check out time _____
- ❑ Dog friendly _____Y _____N
- ❑ Max RV length _____
- ❑ Distance from home

    miles: _____

    hours: _____

- ❑ Address_____

    _____

    _____

Fees:

- ❑ Day Use $ _____
- ❑ Camp Sites $_____
- ❑ RV Sites $ _____
- ❑ Refund policy

    _____

    _____

    _____

Make It Personal

Trip dates: _____

Why I went: _____

I went with: _____

How I got there: (circle all that apply) Plane   Train   Car   Bus   Bike   Hike   RV   MC

We stayed in (space, cabin, etc.)

_____

The weather was: Sunny   Cloudy   Rainy   Stormy   Snowy   Foggy   Warm   Cold

Most relaxing day:

_____

Something funny:

_____

Someone we met:

_____

Best story told:

_____

The kids liked this:

_____

The best food:

_____

Games played:

_____

Something disappointing:

_____

Next time I'll do this differently:

_____

Lake Kissimmee State Park
City: Lake Wales   County: Polk

Plan your Trip https://www.floridastateparks.org/parks-and-trails/lake-kissimmee-state-park

Activities:

- ❑ Beach Access
- ❑ Biking Trails
- ❑ Boating
- ❑ Campfire
- ❑ Caving
- ❑ Disc Golf
- ❑ Fishing
- ❑ Geo Cache
- ❑ Golf
- ❑ Hiking
- ❑ Horseback

- ❑ Hunting
- ❑ OHV
- ❑ Park Tours
- ❑ Rock Climbing
- ❑ Snorkeling
- ❑ Stargazing
- ❑ Swimming
- ❑ Viewpoint
- ❑ Wildlife & Birding
- ❑
- ❑

Facilities:

- ❑ ADA
- ❑ Gym
- ❑ Historic Sites
- ❑ Lodge
- ❑ Meeting Hall
- ❑ Pavilions
- ❑ Picnic sites
- ❑ Pool
- ❑ Restrooms

- ❑ Showers
- ❑ Visitor Center
- ❑ RV Camp
- ❑ Tent Camp
- ❑ Cabins
- ❑ Lodge Rooms
- ❑
- ❑
- ❑

Notes:

Get the Facts

- ❑ Phone: 863-696-1112
- ❑ Park Hours

    _____

- ❑ Reservations? ____Y ____N

    date made_____

- ❑ Open year 'round ___Y___N

    dates_____

- ❑ Check in time _____
- ❑ Check out time _____
- ❑ Dog friendly _____Y _____N
- ❑ Max RV length _____
- ❑ Distance from home

    miles: _____

    hours: _____

- ❑ Address_____

    _____

    _____

Fees:

- ❑ Day Use $ _____
- ❑ Camp Sites $_____
- ❑ RV Sites $ _____
- ❑ Refund policy

    _____

    _____

    _____

Make It Personal

Trip dates:

Why I went:

I went with:

How I got there: (circle all that apply) Plane   Train   Car   Bus   Bike   Hike   RV   MC

We stayed in (space, cabin, etc.)

The weather was: Sunny   Cloudy   Rainy   Stormy   Snowy   Foggy   Warm   Cold

Most relaxing day:

Something funny:

Someone we met:

Best story told:

The kids liked this:

The best food:

Games played:

Something disappointing:

Next time I'll do this differently:

Colt Creek State Park
City: Lakeland   County: Polk

Plan your Trip https://www.floridastateparks.org/parks-and-trails/colt-creek-state-park

Activities:

- ❑ Beach Access
- ❑ Biking Trails
- ❑ Boating
- ❑ Campfire
- ❑ Caving
- ❑ Disc Golf
- ❑ Fishing
- ❑ Geo Cache
- ❑ Golf
- ❑ Hiking
- ❑ Horseback

- ❑ Hunting
- ❑ OHV
- ❑ Park Tours
- ❑ Rock Climbing
- ❑ Snorkeling
- ❑ Stargazing
- ❑ Swimming
- ❑ Viewpoint
- ❑ Wildlife & Birding
- ❑
- ❑

Facilities:

- ❑ ADA
- ❑ Gym
- ❑ Historic Sites
- ❑ Lodge
- ❑ Meeting Hall
- ❑ Pavilions
- ❑ Picnic sites
- ❑ Pool
- ❑ Restrooms

- ❑ Showers
- ❑ Visitor Center
- ❑ RV Camp
- ❑ Tent Camp
- ❑ Cabins
- ❑ Lodge Rooms
- ❑
- ❑
- ❑

Notes:

Get the Facts

- ❑ Phone: 863-815-6761
- ❑ Park Hours

  _____

- ❑ Reservations? _____Y _____N

  date made_____

- ❑ Open year 'round ___Y___N

  dates_____

- ❑ Check in time _____

- ❑ Check out time _____

- ❑ Dog friendly _____Y _____N

- ❑ Max RV length _____

- ❑ Distance from home

  miles: _____

  hours: _____

- ❑ Address_____

  _____

  _____

Fees:

- ❑ Day Use $ _____
- ❑ Camp Sites $_____
- ❑ RV Sites $ _____
- ❑ Refund policy

  _____

  _____

  _____

Make It Personal

Trip dates:

Why I went:

I went with:

How I got there: (circle all that apply) Plane   Train   Car   Bus   Bike   Hike   RV   MC

We stayed in (space, cabin, etc.)

The weather was: Sunny   Cloudy   Rainy   Stormy   Snowy   Foggy   Warm   Cold

Most relaxing day:

Something funny:

Someone we met:

Best story told:

The kids liked this:

The best food:

Games played:

Something disappointing:

Next time I'll do this differently:

Lower Wekiva River Preserve State Park
City: Sanford   County: Seminole

Plan your Trip https://www.floridastateparks.org/index.php/parks-and-trails/lower-wekiva-river-preserve-state-park

Activities:

- ❑ Beach Access
- ❑ Biking Trails
- ❑ Boating
- ❑ Campfire
- ❑ Caving
- ❑ Disc Golf
- ❑ Fishing
- ❑ Geo Cache
- ❑ Golf
- ❑ Hiking
- ❑ Horseback

- ❑ Hunting
- ❑ OHV
- ❑ Park Tours
- ❑ Rock Climbing
- ❑ Snorkeling
- ❑ Stargazing
- ❑ Swimming
- ❑ Viewpoint
- ❑ Wildlife & Birding
- ❑
- ❑

Facilities:

- ❑ ADA
- ❑ Gym
- ❑ Historic Sites
- ❑ Lodge
- ❑ Meeting Hall
- ❑ Pavilions
- ❑ Picnic sites
- ❑ Pool
- ❑ Restrooms

- ❑ Showers
- ❑ Visitor Center
- ❑ RV Camp
- ❑ Tent Camp
- ❑ Cabins
- ❑ Lodge Rooms
- ❑
- ❑
- ❑

Notes:

Get the Facts

- ❑ Phone: 407-553-4383
- ❑ Park Hours

  _____

- ❑ Reservations? ____Y ____N

  date made_____

- ❑ Open year 'round ___Y___N

  dates_____

- ❑ Check in time _____
- ❑ Check out time _____
- ❑ Dog friendly _____Y _____N
- ❑ Max RV length _____
- ❑ Distance from home

  miles: _____

  hours: _____

- ❑ Address_____

  _____

  _____

Fees:

- ❑ Day Use $ _____
- ❑ Camp Sites $_____
- ❑ RV Sites $ _____
- ❑ Refund policy

  _____

  _____

  _____

Make It Personal

Trip dates: _____

Why I went: _____

I went with: _____

How I got there: (circle all that apply) Plane   Train   Car   Bus   Bike   Hike   RV   MC

We stayed in (space, cabin, etc.) _____

The weather was: Sunny   Cloudy   Rainy   Stormy   Snowy   Foggy   Warm   Cold

Most relaxing day: _____

_____

Something funny: _____

_____

Someone we met: _____

_____

Best story told: _____

_____

The kids liked this: _____

The best food: _____

Games played: _____

Something disappointing: _____

Next time I'll do this differently: _____

Paynes Creek Historic State Park
City: Bowling Green   County: Hardee

Plan your trip https://www.floridastateparks.org/parks-and-trails/paynes-creek-historic-state-park

Activities:

- ❑ Birding / Wildlife
- ❑ Fishing
- ❑ Guided tours
- ❑ Geo cache
- ❑ Hiking
- ❑ Horseback
- ❑ Hunting
- ❑ Snorkeling
- ❑ Trails
- ❑ Water access

Facilities:

- ❑ ADA
- ❑ Meeting hall
- ❑ Pavilions
- ❑ Picnic sites
- ❑ Restrooms
- ❑ Visitor center
- ❑
- ❑
- ❑
- ❑

Get the Facts

- ❑ Phone 863-375-4717
- ❑ Park Hours

   _____

- ❑ Reservations? ____Y ____N

   date made_____

- ❑ Open year 'round ___Y___N

   dates_____

- ❑ Distance from home

   miles: _____

   hours: _____

- ❑ Address or GPS

   _____

   _____

Date visited:

I went with:
_____

My favorite things:
_____

_____

_____

Fees:

- ❑ Day Use $ _____
- ❑ Parking $_____
- ❑ Refund policy

   _____

   _____

Notes

Lake June-in-Winter Scrub Preserve SP
City: Lake Placid   County: Highlands

Plan your trip https://www.floridastateparks.org/index.php/parks-and-trails/lake-june-winter-scrub-preserve-state-park

Activities:

- ❑ Birding / Wildlife
- ❑ Fishing
- ❑ Guided tours
- ❑ Geo cache
- ❑ Hiking
- ❑ Horseback
- ❑ Hunting
- ❑ Snorkeling
- ❑ Trails
- ❑ Water access

Facilities:

- ❑ ADA
- ❑ Meeting hall
- ❑ Pavilions
- ❑ Picnic sites
- ❑ Restrooms
- ❑ Visitor center
- ❑
- ❑
- ❑
- ❑

Get the Facts

- ❑ Phone 863-386-6094
- ❑ Park Hours

  _____

- ❑ Reservations? ____Y ____N

  date made_____

- ❑ Open year 'round ___Y___N

  dates_____

- ❑ Distance from home

  miles: _____

  hours: _____

- ❑ Address or GPS

  _____

  _____

Date visited:

I went with:

_____

My favorite things:

_____

_____

_____

Notes

Fees:

- ❑ Day Use $ _____
- ❑ Parking $_____
- ❑ Refund policy

  _____

  _____

Historic Santos Recreation Area
City: Ocala   County: Marion

Plan your trip https://www.floridastateparks.org/parks-and-trails/historic-santos-recreation-area

Activities:

- ❏ Birding / Wildlife
- ❏ Fishing
- ❏ Guided tours
- ❏ Geo cache
- ❏ Hiking
- ❏ Horseback
- ❏ Hunting
- ❏ Snorkeling
- ❏ Trails
- ❏ Water access

Facilities:

- ❏ ADA
- ❏ Meeting hall
- ❏ Pavilions
- ❏ Picnic sites
- ❏ Restrooms
- ❏ Visitor center
- ❏
- ❏
- ❏
- ❏

Get the Facts

- ❏ Phone 352-236-7143
- ❏ Park Hours

  _____

- ❏ Reservations? ____Y ____N

  date made_____

- ❏ Open year 'round ___Y___N

  dates_____

- ❏ Distance from home

  miles: _____

  hours: _____

- ❏ Address or GPS

  _____

  _____

Date visited:

I went with:
_____

My favorite things:
_____
_____
_____
_____

Fees:

- ❏ Day Use $ _____
- ❏ Parking $_____
- ❏ Refund policy

  _____

  _____

Notes

Wekiwa Springs State Park
City: Apopka   County: Orange

Plan your trip https://www.floridastateparks.org/parks-and-trails/wekiwa-springs-state-park

Activities:

- ❏ Birding / Wildlife
- ❏ Fishing
- ❏ Guided tours
- ❏ Geo cache
- ❏ Hiking
- ❏ Horseback
- ❏ Hunting
- ❏ Snorkeling
- ❏ Trails
- ❏ Water access

Facilities:

- ❏ ADA
- ❏ Meeting hall
- ❏ Pavilions
- ❏ Picnic sites
- ❏ Restrooms
- ❏ Visitor center
- ❏
- ❏
- ❏
- ❏

Get the Facts

- ❏ Phone 407-553-4383
- ❏ Park Hours

  _____

- ❏ Reservations? ____Y ____N

  date made_____

- ❏ Open year 'round ___Y___N

  dates_____

- ❏ Distance from home

  miles: _____

  hours: _____

- ❏ Address or GPS

  _____

  _____

Date visited:

I went with:
_____

My favorite things:
_____

_____

_____

Fees:

- ❏ Day Use $ _____
- ❏ Parking $_____
- ❏ Refund policy

  _____

  _____

Notes

Allen David Broussard Catfish Creek Preserve SP
City: Haines City   County: Polk

Plan your trip https://www.floridastateparks.org/parks-and-trails/allen-david-broussard-catfish-creek-preserve-state-park

Activities:

- ❑ Birding / Wildlife
- ❑ Fishing
- ❑ Guided tours
- ❑ Geo cache
- ❑ Hiking
- ❑ Horseback
- ❑ Hunting
- ❑ Snorkeling
- ❑ Trails
- ❑ Water access

Facilities:

- ❑ ADA
- ❑ Meeting hall
- ❑ Pavilions
- ❑ Picnic sites
- ❑ Restrooms
- ❑ Visitor center
- ❑
- ❑
- ❑
- ❑

Get the Facts

- ❑ Phone 863-696-1112
- ❑ Park Hours

    _____

- ❑ Reservations? ____Y ____N

    date made_____

- ❑ Open year 'round ___Y___N

    dates_____

- ❑ Distance from home

    miles: _____

    hours: _____

- ❑ Address or GPS

    _____

    _____

Date visited:

I went with:
_____

My favorite things:
_____

_____

_____

Notes

Fees:

- ❑ Day Use $ _____
- ❑ Parking $_____
- ❑ Refund policy

    _____

    _____

Dade Battlefield Memorial SP
City: Bushnell   County: Sumter

Plan your trip https://www.floridastateparks.org/parks-and-trails/dade-battlefield-historic-state-park

Activities:

- ❑ Birding / Wildlife
- ❑ Fishing
- ❑ Guided tours
- ❑ Geo cache
- ❑ Hiking
- ❑ Horseback
- ❑ Hunting
- ❑ Snorkeling
- ❑ Trails
- ❑ Water access

Facilities:

- ❑ ADA
- ❑ Meeting hall
- ❑ Pavilions
- ❑ Picnic sites
- ❑ Restrooms
- ❑ Visitor center
- ❑
- ❑
- ❑
- ❑

Get the Facts

- ❑ Phone 352-793-4781
- ❑ Park Hours

  _____

- ❑ Reservations? _____Y _____N

  date made_____

- ❑ Open year 'round ___Y___N

  dates_____

- ❑ Distance from home

  miles: _____

  hours: _____

- ❑ Address or GPS

  _____

  _____

Date visited:

I went with:

_____

My favorite things:

_____

_____

_____

Fees:

- ❑ Day Use $ _____
- ❑ Parking $_____
- ❑ Refund policy

  _____

  _____

Notes

Florida State Park Trivia

1. One of the state parks is only 1 acre in size, which one is it?.
A. Eden Gardens State Park
B. Gamble Plantation Historic State Park
C. Madison Blue Spring State Park

2. Name the largest Florida State Park by acre area.
A. Charlotte Harbor Preserve SP
B. Kissimmee Prairie Preserve SP
C. Fakahatchee Strand Preserve SP

3. What is the service mark (SM) of Florida State Parks?
A. Adventure In Every Corner
B. The Real Florida
C. People Make the Parks

4. Name the tallest archaeological ceremonial mound in Florida
A. Letchworth-Love Mounds ASP
B. Mound Key Archaeological State Park
C. Crystal River Archaeological SP

5. Which is the deepest freshwater spring in Florida?
A. Big Lagoon State Park
B. Madison Blue Spring State Park
C. Edward Ball Wakulla Springs

6. What are the largest Whitewater rapids in Florida?
A. Big Shoals State Park
B. St Marks River Preserve SP
C. Oleta River State Park

7. Largest underwater cave system in the continental US is in Florida, there?
A. Wes Sikes Peacock Springs State Park
B. John Pennekamp Coral Reef SP
C. Florida Caverns State Park

8. Name the highest waterfall in a Florida State Park
A. Lafayette Blue Springs State Park
B. Falling Waters State Park
C. Ichetucknee Springs State Park

9. What is the only state park in Florida that allows horseback riding on the beach?
A. Amelia Island State Park
B. Hontoon Island State Park
C. Perdido Key State Park

10. Which is the newest Florida State Park?
A. Crystal River Preserve SP
B. Fort Mose Historic State Park
C. Gilchrist Blue Springs SP

Key: 1=C, 2=C, 3=B 4=B, 5=A, 6=C, 7=A, 8=A 9=B, 10=C

190

Central East

- Brevard
- Indian River
- Okeechobee
- St. Lucie
- Volusia

Sebastian Inlet State Park
City: Melbourne Beach   County: Brevard

Plan your Trip https://www.floridastateparks.org/parks-and-trails/sebastian-inlet-state-park

Activities:

- ❏ Beach Access
- ❏ Biking Trails
- ❏ Boating
- ❏ Campfire
- ❏ Caving
- ❏ Disc Golf
- ❏ Fishing
- ❏ Geo Cache
- ❏ Golf
- ❏ Hiking
- ❏ Horseback

- ❏ Hunting
- ❏ OHV
- ❏ Park Tours
- ❏ Rock Climbing
- ❏ Snorkeling
- ❏ Stargazing
- ❏ Swimming
- ❏ Viewpoint
- ❏ Wildlife & Birding
- ❏
- ❏

Facilities:

- ❏ ADA
- ❏ Gym
- ❏ Historic Sites
- ❏ Lodge
- ❏ Meeting Hall
- ❏ Pavilions
- ❏ Picnic sites
- ❏ Pool
- ❏ Restrooms

- ❏ Showers
- ❏ Visitor Center
- ❏ RV Camp
- ❏ Tent Camp
- ❏ Cabins
- ❏ Lodge Rooms
- ❏
- ❏
- ❏

Notes:

Get the Facts

- ❏ Phone: 321-984-4852
- ❏ Park Hours

  _____

- ❏ Reservations? ____Y ____N

  date made_____

- ❏ Open year 'round ___Y___N

  dates_____

- ❏ Check in time _____
- ❏ Check out time _____
- ❏ Dog friendly _____Y _____N
- ❏ Max RV length _____
- ❏ Distance from home

  miles: _____

  hours: _____

- ❏ Address_____

  _____

  _____

Fees:

- ❏ Day Use $ _____
- ❏ Camp Sites $_____
- ❏ RV Sites $ _____
- ❏ Refund policy

  _____

  _____

  _____

Make It Personal

Trip dates: _____

Why I went: _____

I went with: _____

How I got there: (circle all that apply) Plane   Train   Car   Bus   Bike   Hike   RV   MC

We stayed in (space, cabin, etc.) _____

The weather was: Sunny   Cloudy   Rainy   Stormy   Snowy   Foggy   Warm   Cold

Most relaxing day: _____

Something funny: _____

Someone we met: _____

Best story told: _____

The kids liked this: _____

The best food: _____

Games played: _____

Something disappointing: _____

Next time I'll do this differently: _____

St. Sebastian River Preserve State Park

City: Fellsmere   **County: Indian River**

Plan your Trip https://www.floridastateparks.org/parks-and-trails/st-sebastian-river-preserve-state-park

Activities:

- ❑ Beach Access
- ❑ Biking Trails
- ❑ Boating
- ❑ Campfire
- ❑ Caving
- ❑ Disc Golf
- ❑ Fishing
- ❑ Geo Cache
- ❑ Golf
- ❑ Hiking
- ❑ Horseback

- ❑ Hunting
- ❑ OHV
- ❑ Park Tours
- ❑ Rock Climbing
- ❑ Snorkeling
- ❑ Stargazing
- ❑ Swimming
- ❑ Viewpoint
- ❑ Wildlife & Birding
- ❑
- ❑

Facilities:

- ❑ ADA
- ❑ Gym
- ❑ Historic Sites
- ❑ Lodge
- ❑ Meeting Hall
- ❑ Pavilions
- ❑ Picnic sites
- ❑ Pool
- ❑ Restrooms

- ❑ Showers
- ❑ Visitor Center
- ❑ RV Camp
- ❑ Tent Camp
- ❑ Cabins
- ❑ Lodge Rooms
- ❑
- ❑
- ❑

Notes:

Get the Facts

- ❑ Phone: 321-984-4852
- ❑ Park Hours

  _____

- ❑ Reservations? ____Y ____N

  date made_____

- ❑ Open year 'round ___Y___N

  dates_____

- ❑ Check in time _____
- ❑ Check out time _____
- ❑ Dog friendly _____Y _____N
- ❑ Max RV length _____
- ❑ Distance from home

  miles: _____

  hours: _____

- ❑ Address_____

  _____

  _____

Fees:

- ❑ Day Use $ _____
- ❑ Camp Sites $_____
- ❑ RV Sites $ _____
- ❑ Refund policy

  _____

  _____

  _____

Make It Personal

Trip dates: _____

Why I went: _____

I went with: _____

How I got there: (circle all that apply) Plane   Train   Car   Bus   Bike   Hike   RV   MC

We stayed in (space, cabin, etc.) _____

The weather was: Sunny   Cloudy   Rainy   Stormy   Snowy   Foggy   Warm   Cold

Most relaxing day: _____

Something funny: _____

Someone we met: _____

Best story told: _____

The kids liked this: _____

The best food: _____

Games played: _____

Something disappointing: _____

Next time I'll do this differently: _____

Kissimmee Prairie Preserve State Park
City: Okeechobee   County: Okeechobee

Plan your Trip https://www.floridastateparks.org/parks-and-trails/kissimmee-prairie-preserve-state-park

Activities:

- ❑ Beach Access
- ❑ Biking Trails
- ❑ Boating
- ❑ Campfire
- ❑ Caving
- ❑ Disc Golf
- ❑ Fishing
- ❑ Geo Cache
- ❑ Golf
- ❑ Hiking
- ❑ Horseback

- ❑ Hunting
- ❑ OHV
- ❑ Park Tours
- ❑ Rock Climbing
- ❑ Snorkeling
- ❑ Stargazing
- ❑ Swimming
- ❑ Viewpoint
- ❑ Wildlife & Birding
- ❑
- ❑

Facilities:

- ❑ ADA
- ❑ Gym
- ❑ Historic Sites
- ❑ Lodge
- ❑ Meeting Hall
- ❑ Pavilions
- ❑ Picnic sites
- ❑ Pool
- ❑ Restrooms

- ❑ Showers
- ❑ Visitor Center
- ❑ RV Camp
- ❑ Tent Camp
- ❑ Cabins
- ❑ Lodge Rooms
- ❑
- ❑
- ❑

Notes:

Get the Facts

- ❑ Phone: 863-462-5360
- ❑ Park Hours

  _____

- ❑ Reservations? _____Y _____N

  date made_____

- ❑ Open year 'round ___Y___N

  dates_____

- ❑ Check in time _____

- ❑ Check out time _____

- ❑ Dog friendly _____Y _____N

- ❑ Max RV length _____

- ❑ Distance from home

  miles: _____

  hours: _____

- ❑ Address_____

  _____

  _____

Fees:

- ❑ Day Use $ _____
- ❑ Camp Sites $_____
- ❑ RV Sites $ _____
- ❑ Refund policy

  _____

  _____

  _____

Make It Personal

Trip dates:

Why I went:

I went with:

How I got there: (circle all that apply) Plane   Train   Car   Bus   Bike   Hike   RV   MC

We stayed in (space, cabin, etc.)

The weather was: Sunny   Cloudy   Rainy   Stormy   Snowy   Foggy   Warm   Cold

Most relaxing day:

Something funny:

Someone we met:

Best story told:

The kids liked this:

The best food:

Games played:

Something disappointing:

Next time I'll do this differently:

Fort Pierce Inlet State Park
City: Fort Pierce   County: St. Lucie

Plan your Trip https://www.floridastateparks.org/index.php/parks-and-trails/fort-pierce-inlet-state-park

Activities:

- ❑ Beach Access
- ❑ Biking Trails
- ❑ Boating
- ❑ Campfire
- ❑ Caving
- ❑ Disc Golf
- ❑ Fishing
- ❑ Geo Cache
- ❑ Golf
- ❑ Hiking
- ❑ Horseback

- ❑ Hunting
- ❑ OHV
- ❑ Park Tours
- ❑ Rock Climbing
- ❑ Snorkeling
- ❑ Stargazing
- ❑ Swimming
- ❑ Viewpoint
- ❑ Wildlife & Birding
- ❑
- ❑

Facilities:

- ❑ ADA
- ❑ Gym
- ❑ Historic Sites
- ❑ Lodge
- ❑ Meeting Hall
- ❑ Pavilions
- ❑ Picnic sites
- ❑ Pool
- ❑ Restrooms

- ❑ Showers
- ❑ Visitor Center
- ❑ RV Camp
- ❑ Tent Camp
- ❑ Cabins
- ❑ Lodge Rooms
- ❑
- ❑
- ❑

Notes:

Get the Facts

- ❑ Phone: 772-468-3985
- ❑ Park Hours

  _____

- ❑ Reservations? ____Y ____N

  date made_____

- ❑ Open year 'round ___Y___N

  dates_____

- ❑ Check in time _____
- ❑ Check out time _____
- ❑ Dog friendly _____Y _____N
- ❑ Max RV length _____
- ❑ Distance from home

  miles: _____

  hours: _____

- ❑ Address_____

  _____

  _____

Fees:

- ❑ Day Use $ _____
- ❑ Camp Sites $_____
- ❑ RV Sites $ _____
- ❑ Refund policy

  _____

  _____

  _____

Make It Personal

Trip dates:

Why I went:

I went with:

How I got there: (circle all that apply) Plane   Train   Car   Bus   Bike   Hike   RV   MC

We stayed in (space, cabin, etc.)

The weather was: Sunny Cloudy Rainy Stormy Snowy Foggy Warm Cold

Most relaxing day:

Something funny:

Someone we met:

Best story told:

The kids liked this:

The best food:

Games played:

Something disappointing:

Next time I'll do this differently:

Hontoon Island State Park
City: DeLand   County: Volusia

Plan your Trip https://www.floridastateparks.org/parks-and-trails/hontoon-island-state-park

Activities:

- ❑ Beach Access
- ❑ Biking Trails
- ❑ Boating
- ❑ Campfire
- ❑ Caving
- ❑ Disc Golf
- ❑ Fishing
- ❑ Geo Cache
- ❑ Golf
- ❑ Hiking
- ❑ Horseback

- ❑ Hunting
- ❑ OHV
- ❑ Park Tours
- ❑ Rock Climbing
- ❑ Snorkeling
- ❑ Stargazing
- ❑ Swimming
- ❑ Viewpoint
- ❑ Wildlife & Birding
- ❑
- ❑

Facilities:

- ❑ ADA
- ❑ Gym
- ❑ Historic Sites
- ❑ Lodge
- ❑ Meeting Hall
- ❑ Pavilions
- ❑ Picnic sites
- ❑ Pool
- ❑ Restrooms

- ❑ Showers
- ❑ Visitor Center
- ❑ RV Camp
- ❑ Tent Camp
- ❑ Cabins
- ❑ Lodge Rooms
- ❑
- ❑
- ❑

Notes:

Get the Facts

- ❑ Phone: 386-736-5309
- ❑ Park Hours

  _____

- ❑ Reservations? ____Y ____N

  date made_____

- ❑ Open year 'round ___Y___N

  dates_____

- ❑ Check in time _____

- ❑ Check out time _____

- ❑ Dog friendly _____Y _____N

- ❑ Max RV length _____

- ❑ Distance from home

  miles: _____

  hours: _____

- ❑ Address_____

  _____

  _____

Fees:

- ❑ Day Use $ _____
- ❑ Camp Sites $_____
- ❑ RV Sites $ _____
- ❑ Refund policy

  _____

  _____

  _____

Make It Personal

Trip dates: _____

Why I went: _____

I went with: _____

How I got there: (circle all that apply) Plane   Train   Car   Bus   Bike   Hike   RV   MC

We stayed in (space, cabin, etc.) _____

_____

The weather was: Sunny Cloudy Rainy Stormy Snowy Foggy Warm Cold

Most relaxing day: _____

_____

Something funny: _____

_____

Someone we met: _____

_____

Best story told: _____

_____

The kids liked this: _____

The best food: _____

_____

Games played: _____

_____

Something disappointing: _____

_____

Next time I'll do this differently: _____

_____

201

Blue Spring State Park
City: Orange City   County: Volusia

Plan your Trip https://www.floridastateparks.org/parks-and-trails/blue-spring-state-park

Activities:

- ❑ Beach Access
- ❑ Biking Trails
- ❑ Boating
- ❑ Campfire
- ❑ Caving
- ❑ Disc Golf
- ❑ Fishing
- ❑ Geo Cache
- ❑ Golf
- ❑ Hiking
- ❑ Horseback

- ❑ Hunting
- ❑ OHV
- ❑ Park Tours
- ❑ Rock Climbing
- ❑ Snorkeling
- ❑ Stargazing
- ❑ Swimming
- ❑ Viewpoint
- ❑ Wildlife & Birding
- ❑
- ❑

Facilities:

- ❑ ADA
- ❑ Gym
- ❑ Historic Sites
- ❑ Lodge
- ❑ Meeting Hall
- ❑ Pavilions
- ❑ Picnic sites
- ❑ Pool
- ❑ Restrooms

- ❑ Showers
- ❑ Visitor Center
- ❑ RV Camp
- ❑ Tent Camp
- ❑ Cabins
- ❑ Lodge Rooms
- ❑
- ❑
- ❑

Notes:

Get the Facts

- ❑ Phone: 386-775-3663
- ❑ Park Hours

  _____

- ❑ Reservations? ____Y ____N

  date made_____

- ❑ Open year 'round ___Y___N

  dates_____

- ❑ Check in time _____
- ❑ Check out time _____
- ❑ Dog friendly _____Y _____N
- ❑ Max RV length _____
- ❑ Distance from home

  miles: _____

  hours: _____

- ❑ Address_____

  _____

  _____

Fees:

- ❑ Day Use $ _____
- ❑ Camp Sites $_____
- ❑ RV Sites $ _____
- ❑ Refund policy

  _____

  _____

  _____

Make It Personal

Trip dates:

Why I went:

I went with:

How I got there: (circle all that apply) Plane   Train   Car   Bus   Bike   Hike   RV   MC

We stayed in (space, cabin, etc.)

The weather was: Sunny   Cloudy   Rainy   Stormy   Snowy   Foggy   Warm   Cold

Most relaxing day:

Something funny:

Someone we met:

Best story told:

The kids liked this:

The best food:

Games played:

Something disappointing:

Next time I'll do this differently:

Bulow Creek State Park
City: Ormond Beach   County: Volusia

Plan your Trip https://www.floridastateparks.org/parks-and-trails/bulow-creek-state-park

Activities:

- ❑ Beach Access
- ❑ Biking Trails
- ❑ Boating
- ❑ Campfire
- ❑ Caving
- ❑ Disc Golf
- ❑ Fishing
- ❑ Geo Cache
- ❑ Golf
- ❑ Hiking
- ❑ Horseback

- ❑ Hunting
- ❑ OHV
- ❑ Park Tours
- ❑ Rock Climbing
- ❑ Snorkeling
- ❑ Stargazing
- ❑ Swimming
- ❑ Viewpoint
- ❑ Wildlife & Birding
- ❑
- ❑

Facilities:

- ❑ ADA
- ❑ Gym
- ❑ Historic Sites
- ❑ Lodge
- ❑ Meeting Hall
- ❑ Pavilions
- ❑ Picnic sites
- ❑ Pool
- ❑ Restrooms

- ❑ Showers
- ❑ Visitor Center
- ❑ RV Camp
- ❑ Tent Camp
- ❑ Cabins
- ❑ Lodge Rooms
- ❑
- ❑
- ❑

Notes:

Get the Facts

- ❑ Phone: 386-676-4050
- ❑ Park Hours

  _____

- ❑ Reservations? ____Y ____N

  date made_____

- ❑ Open year 'round ___Y___N

  dates_____

- ❑ Check in time _____

- ❑ Check out time _____

- ❑ Dog friendly _____Y _____N

- ❑ Max RV length _____

- ❑ Distance from home

  miles: _____

  hours: _____

- ❑ Address_____

  _____

  _____

Fees:

- ❑ Day Use $ _____
- ❑ Camp Sites $_____
- ❑ RV Sites $ _____
- ❑ Refund policy

  _____

  _____

  _____

Make It Personal

Trip dates: _____

Why I went: _____

I went with: _____

How I got there: (circle all that apply) Plane Train Car Bus Bike Hike RV MC

We stayed in (space, cabin, etc.) _____

The weather was: Sunny Cloudy Rainy Stormy Snowy Foggy Warm Cold

Most relaxing day: _____

Something funny: _____

Someone we met: _____

Best story told: _____

The kids liked this: _____

The best food: _____

Games played: _____

Something disappointing: _____

Next time I'll do this differently: _____

Tomoka State Park
City: Ormond Beach   County: Volusia

Plan your Trip https://www.floridastateparks.org/Tomoka

Activities:

- ❑ Beach Access
- ❑ Biking Trails
- ❑ Boating
- ❑ Campfire
- ❑ Caving
- ❑ Disc Golf
- ❑ Fishing
- ❑ Geo Cache
- ❑ Golf
- ❑ Hiking
- ❑ Horseback

- ❑ Hunting
- ❑ OHV
- ❑ Park Tours
- ❑ Rock Climbing
- ❑ Snorkeling
- ❑ Stargazing
- ❑ Swimming
- ❑ Viewpoint
- ❑ Wildlife & Birding
- ❑
- ❑

Facilities:

- ❑ ADA
- ❑ Gym
- ❑ Historic Sites
- ❑ Lodge
- ❑ Meeting Hall
- ❑ Pavilions
- ❑ Picnic sites
- ❑ Pool
- ❑ Restrooms

- ❑ Showers
- ❑ Visitor Center
- ❑ RV Camp
- ❑ Tent Camp
- ❑ Cabins
- ❑ Lodge Rooms
- ❑
- ❑
- ❑

Notes:

Get the Facts

- ❑ Phone: 386-676-4050
- ❑ Park Hours

  _____

- ❑ Reservations? ____Y ____N

  date made_____

- ❑ Open year 'round ___Y___N

  dates_____

- ❑ Check in time _____
- ❑ Check out time _____
- ❑ Dog friendly _____Y _____N
- ❑ Max RV length _____
- ❑ Distance from home

  miles: _____

  hours: _____

- ❑ Address_____

  _____

  _____

Fees:

- ❑ Day Use $ _____
- ❑ Camp Sites $_____
- ❑ RV Sites $ _____
- ❑ Refund policy

  _____

  _____

  _____

Make It Personal

Trip dates:

Why I went:

I went with:

How I got there: (circle all that apply) Plane   Train   Car   Bus   Bike   Hike   RV   MC

We stayed in (space, cabin, etc.)

The weather was: Sunny   Cloudy   Rainy   Stormy   Snowy   Foggy   Warm   Cold

Most relaxing day:

Something funny:

Someone we met:

Best story told:

The kids liked this:

The best food:

Games played:

Something disappointing:

Next time I'll do this differently:

Indian River Lagoon Preserve SP
City: Indian River   County: Indian River

Plan your trip https://www.floridastateparks.org/index.php/parks-and-trails/indian-river-lagoon-preserve-state-park

Activities:

- ❑ Birding / Wildlife
- ❑ Fishing
- ❑ Guided tours
- ❑ Geo cache
- ❑ Hiking
- ❑ Horseback
- ❑ Hunting
- ❑ Snorkeling
- ❑ Trails
- ❑ Water access

Facilities:

- ❑ ADA
- ❑ Meeting hall
- ❑ Pavilions
- ❑ Picnic sites
- ❑ Restrooms
- ❑ Visitor center
- ❑
- ❑
- ❑
- ❑

Get the Facts

- ❑ Phone 321-984-4852
- ❑ Park Hours

  _____

- ❑ Reservations? ____Y ____N

  date made_____

- ❑ Open year 'round ___Y___N

  dates_____

- ❑ Distance from home

  miles: _____

  hours: _____

- ❑ Address or GPS

  _____

  _____

Date visited:

I went with:
_____

My favorite things:
_____

_____

_____

Notes

Fees:

- ❑ Day Use $ _____
- ❑ Parking $_____
- ❑ Refund policy

  _____

  _____

Okeechobee Battlefield Historic SP
City: Okeechobee   County: Okeechobee

Plan your trip https://www.floridastateparks.org/index.php/parks-and-trails/okeechobee-battlefield-historic-state-park

Activities:

- ❑ Birding / Wildlife
- ❑ Fishing
- ❑ Guided tours
- ❑ Geo cache
- ❑ Hiking
- ❑ Horseback
- ❑ Hunting
- ❑ Snorkeling
- ❑ Trails
- ❑ Water access

Facilities:

- ❑ ADA
- ❑ Meeting hall
- ❑ Pavilions
- ❑ Picnic sites
- ❑ Restrooms
- ❑ Visitor center
- ❑
- ❑
- ❑
- ❑

Get the Facts

- ❑ Phone 863-462-5360
- ❑ Park Hours

  _____

- ❑ Reservations? ____Y ____N

  date made_____

- ❑ Open year 'round ___Y___N

  dates_____

- ❑ Distance from home

  miles: _____

  hours: _____

- ❑ Address or GPS

  _____

  _____

Date visited:

I went with:
_____

My favorite things:
_____

_____

_____

Notes

Fees:

- ❑ Day Use $ _____
- ❑ Parking $_____
- ❑ Refund policy

  _____

  _____

Avalon State Park
City: North Hutchinson Island   County: St. Lucie

Plan your trip https://www.floridastateparks.org/index.php/parks-and-trails/avalon-state-park

Activities:

- ❑ Birding / Wildlife
- ❑ Fishing
- ❑ Guided tours
- ❑ Geo cache
- ❑ Hiking
- ❑ Horseback
- ❑ Hunting
- ❑ Snorkeling
- ❑ Trails
- ❑ Water access

Facilities:

- ❑ ADA
- ❑ Meeting hall
- ❑ Pavilions
- ❑ Picnic sites
- ❑ Restrooms
- ❑ Visitor center
- ❑
- ❑
- ❑
- ❑

Get the Facts

- ❑ Phone 772-468-4007
- ❑ Park Hours

  _____

- ❑ Reservations? ____Y ____N

  date made_____

- ❑ Open year 'round ___Y___N

  dates_____

- ❑ Distance from home

  miles: _____

  hours: _____

- ❑ Address or GPS

  _____

  _____

Date visited:

I went with:
_____

My favorite things:
_____

_____

_____

Fees:

- ❑ Day Use $ _____
- ❑ Parking $_____
- ❑ Refund policy

  _____

  _____

Notes

Savannas Preserve State Park
City: Port St. Lucie   County: St. Lucie

Plan your trip https://www.floridastateparks.org/parks-and-trails/savannas-preserve-state-park

Activities:

- ❑ Birding / Wildlife
- ❑ Fishing
- ❑ Guided tours
- ❑ Geo cache
- ❑ Hiking
- ❑ Horseback
- ❑ Hunting
- ❑ Snorkeling
- ❑ Trails
- ❑ Water access

Facilities:

- ❑ ADA
- ❑ Meeting hall
- ❑ Pavilions
- ❑ Picnic sites
- ❑ Restrooms
- ❑ Visitor center
- ❑
- ❑
- ❑
- ❑

Get the Facts

- ❑ Phone 772-398-2779
- ❑ Park Hours

  _____

- ❑ Reservations? ____Y ____N

  date made_____

- ❑ Open year 'round ___Y___N

  dates_____

- ❑ Distance from home

  miles: _____

  hours: _____

- ❑ Address or GPS

  _____

  _____

Date visited:

I went with:

_____

My favorite things:

_____

_____

_____

Fees:

- ❑ Day Use $ _____
- ❑ Parking $_____
- ❑ Refund policy

  _____

  _____

Notes

De Leon Springs State Park
City: De Leon Springs   County: Volusia

Plan your trip https://www.floridastateparks.org/parks-and-trails/de-leon-springs-state-park

Activities:

- ❏ Birding / Wildlife
- ❏ Fishing
- ❏ Guided tours
- ❏ Geo cache
- ❏ Hiking
- ❏ Horseback
- ❏ Hunting
- ❏ Snorkeling
- ❏ Trails
- ❏ Water access

Facilities:

- ❏ ADA
- ❏ Meeting hall
- ❏ Pavilions
- ❏ Picnic sites
- ❏ Restrooms
- ❏ Visitor center
- ❏
- ❏
- ❏
- ❏

Get the Facts

- ❏ Phone 386-985-4212
- ❏ Park Hours

  _____

- ❏ Reservations? ____Y ____N

  date made_____

- ❏ Open year 'round ___Y___N

  dates_____

- ❏ Distance from home

  miles: _____

  hours: _____

- ❏ Address or GPS

  _____

  _____

Date visited:

I went with:

_____

My favorite things:

_____

_____

_____

Notes

Fees:

- ❏ Day Use $ _____
- ❏ Parking $_____
- ❏ Refund policy

  _____

  _____

Addison Blockhouse Historic State Park
City: Ormond Beach   County: Volusia

Plan your trip https://www.floridastateparks.org/parks-and-trails/addison-blockhouse-historic-state-park

Activities:

- ❑ Birding / Wildlife
- ❑ Fishing
- ❑ Guided tours
- ❑ Geo cache
- ❑ Hiking
- ❑ Horseback
- ❑ Hunting
- ❑ Snorkeling
- ❑ Trails
- ❑ Water access

Facilities:

- ❑ ADA
- ❑ Meeting hall
- ❑ Pavilions
- ❑ Picnic sites
- ❑ Restrooms
- ❑ Visitor center
- ❑
- ❑
- ❑
- ❑

Get the Facts

- ❑ Phone 386-676-4050
- ❑ Park Hours

  _____

- ❑ Reservations? ____Y ____N

  date made_____

- ❑ Open year 'round ___Y___N

  dates_____

- ❑ Distance from home

  miles: _____

  hours: _____

- ❑ Address or GPS

  _____

  _____

Date visited:

I went with:
_____

My favorite things:
_____

_____

_____

Fees:

- ❑ Day Use $ _____
- ❑ Parking $_____
- ❑ Refund policy

  _____

  _____

Notes

Haw Creek Preserve State Park
City: Ormond Beach   County: Volusia

Plan your trip https://www.floridastateparks.org/index.php/parks-and-trails/haw-creek-preserve-state-park

Activities:

- ❑ Birding / Wildlife
- ❑ Fishing
- ❑ Guided tours
- ❑ Geo cache
- ❑ Hiking
- ❑ Horseback
- ❑ Hunting
- ❑ Snorkeling
- ❑ Trails
- ❑ Water access

Facilities:

- ❑ ADA
- ❑ Meeting hall
- ❑ Pavilions
- ❑ Picnic sites
- ❑ Restrooms
- ❑ Visitor center
- ❑
- ❑
- ❑
- ❑

Get the Facts

- ❑ Phone 386-676-4050
- ❑ Park Hours

_____

- ❑ Reservations? ____Y ____N

date made_____

- ❑ Open year 'round ___Y___N

dates_____

- ❑ Distance from home

miles: _____

hours: _____

- ❑ Address or GPS

_____

_____

Date visited:

I went with:
_____

My favorite things:
_____

_____

_____

Notes

Fees:

- ❑ Day Use $ _____
- ❑ Parking $_____
- ❑ Refund policy

_____

_____

North Peninsula State Park
City: Ormond by the Sea   County: Volusia

Plan your trip https://www.floridastateparks.org/parks-and-trails/north-peninsula-state-park

Activities:

- ☐ Birding / Wildlife
- ☐ Fishing
- ☐ Guided tours
- ☐ Geo cache
- ☐ Hiking
- ☐ Horseback
- ☐ Hunting
- ☐ Snorkeling
- ☐ Trails
- ☐ Water access

Facilities:

- ☐ ADA
- ☐ Meeting hall
- ☐ Pavilions
- ☐ Picnic sites
- ☐ Restrooms
- ☐ Visitor center
- ☐
- ☐
- ☐
- ☐

Get the Facts

- ☐ Phone 386-517-2086
- ☐ Park Hours

  _____

- ☐ Reservations? ____Y ____N

  date made_____

- ☐ Open year 'round ___Y___N

  dates_____

- ☐ Distance from home

  miles: _____

  hours: _____

- ☐ Address or GPS

  _____

  _____

Date visited:

I went with:
_____

My favorite things:
_____

_____

_____

Notes

Fees:

- ☐ Day Use $ _____
- ☐ Parking $_____
- ☐ Refund policy

  _____

  _____

Notes:

Southwest

- Charlotte
- Collier
- Lee

Collier-Seminole State Park
City: Naples   County: Collier

Plan your Trip https://www.floridastateparks.org/parks-and-trails/collier-seminole-state-park

Activities:

- ❑ Beach Access
- ❑ Biking Trails
- ❑ Boating
- ❑ Campfire
- ❑ Caving
- ❑ Disc Golf
- ❑ Fishing
- ❑ Geo Cache
- ❑ Golf
- ❑ Hiking
- ❑ Horseback

- ❑ Hunting
- ❑ OHV
- ❑ Park Tours
- ❑ Rock Climbing
- ❑ Snorkeling
- ❑ Stargazing
- ❑ Swimming
- ❑ Viewpoint
- ❑ Wildlife & Birding
- ❑
- ❑

Facilities:

- ❑ ADA
- ❑ Gym
- ❑ Historic Sites
- ❑ Lodge
- ❑ Meeting Hall
- ❑ Pavilions
- ❑ Picnic sites
- ❑ Pool
- ❑ Restrooms

- ❑ Showers
- ❑ Visitor Center
- ❑ RV Camp
- ❑ Tent Camp
- ❑ Cabins
- ❑ Lodge Rooms
- ❑
- ❑
- ❑

Notes:

Get the Facts

- ❑ Phone: 239-394-3397
- ❑ Park Hours

  _____

- ❑ Reservations? ____Y ____N

  date made_____

- ❑ Open year 'round ___Y___N

  dates_____

- ❑ Check in time _____
- ❑ Check out time _____
- ❑ Dog friendly ____Y ____N
- ❑ Max RV length _____
- ❑ Distance from home

  miles: _____

  hours: _____

- ❑ Address_____

  _____

  _____

Fees:

- ❑ Day Use $ _____
- ❑ Camp Sites $_____
- ❑ RV Sites $ _____
- ❑ Refund policy

  _____

  _____

  _____

Make It Personal

Trip dates:

Why I went:

I went with:

How I got there: (circle all that apply) Plane   Train   Car   Bus   Bike   Hike   RV   MC

We stayed in (space, cabin, etc.)

The weather was: Sunny Cloudy Rainy Stormy Snowy Foggy Warm Cold

Most relaxing day:

Something funny:

Someone we met:

Best story told:

The kids liked this:

The best food:

Games played:

Something disappointing:

Next time I'll do this differently:

Cayo Costa State Park
City: Cayo Costa   County: Lee

Plan your Trip https://www.floridastateparks.org/CayoCosta

Activities:

- ❑ Beach Access
- ❑ Biking Trails
- ❑ Boating
- ❑ Campfire
- ❑ Caving
- ❑ Disc Golf
- ❑ Fishing
- ❑ Geo Cache
- ❑ Golf
- ❑ Hiking
- ❑ Horseback

- ❑ Hunting
- ❑ OHV
- ❑ Park Tours
- ❑ Rock Climbing
- ❑ Snorkeling
- ❑ Stargazing
- ❑ Swimming
- ❑ Viewpoint
- ❑ Wildlife & Birding
- ❑
- ❑

Facilities:

- ❑ ADA
- ❑ Gym
- ❑ Historic Sites
- ❑ Lodge
- ❑ Meeting Hall
- ❑ Pavilions
- ❑ Picnic sites
- ❑ Pool
- ❑ Restrooms

- ❑ Showers
- ❑ Visitor Center
- ❑ RV Camp
- ❑ Tent Camp
- ❑ Cabins
- ❑ Lodge Rooms
- ❑
- ❑
- ❑

Notes:

Get the Facts

- ❑ Phone: 941-964-0375
- ❑ Park Hours

  _____

- ❑ Reservations? ____Y ____N

  date made_____

- ❑ Open year 'round ___Y___N

  dates_____

- ❑ Check in time _____

- ❑ Check out time _____

- ❑ Dog friendly _____Y _____N

- ❑ Max RV length _____

- ❑ Distance from home

  miles: _____

  hours: _____

- ❑ Address_____

  _____

  _____

Fees:

- ❑ Day Use $ _____
- ❑ Camp Sites $_____
- ❑ RV Sites $ _____
- ❑ Refund policy

  _____

  _____

  _____

Make It Personal

Trip dates: _____

Why I went: _____

I went with: _____

How I got there: (circle all that apply) Plane   Train   Car   Bus   Bike   Hike   RV   MC

We stayed in (space, cabin, etc.) _____

The weather was: Sunny   Cloudy   Rainy   Stormy   Snowy   Foggy   Warm   Cold

Most relaxing day: _____

Something funny: _____

Someone we met: _____

Best story told: _____

The kids liked this: _____

The best food: _____

Games played: _____

Something disappointing: _____

Next time I'll do this differently: _____

Koreshan State Park
City: Estero   County: Lee

Plan your Trip https://www.floridastateparks.org/index.php/parks-and-trails/koreshan-state-park

Activities:

❑ Beach Access
❑ Biking Trails
❑ Boating
❑ Campfire
❑ Caving
❑ Disc Golf
❑ Fishing
❑ Geo Cache
❑ Golf
❑ Hiking
❑ Horseback

❑ Hunting
❑ OHV
❑ Park Tours
❑ Rock Climbing
❑ Snorkeling
❑ Stargazing
❑ Swimming
❑ Viewpoint
❑ Wildlife & Birding
❑
❑

Facilities:

❑ ADA
❑ Gym
❑ Historic Sites
❑ Lodge
❑ Meeting Hall
❑ Pavilions
❑ Picnic sites
❑ Pool
❑ Restrooms

❑ Showers
❑ Visitor Center
❑ RV Camp
❑ Tent Camp
❑ Cabins
❑ Lodge Rooms
❑
❑
❑

Notes:

Get the Facts

❑ Phone: 239-992-0311
❑ Park Hours

_____

❑ Reservations? ____Y ____N

date made_____

❑ Open year 'round ___Y___N

dates_____

❑ Check in time _____
❑ Check out time _____
❑ Dog friendly _____Y _____N
❑ Max RV length _____
❑ Distance from home

miles: _____

hours: _____

❑ Address_____

_____

_____

Fees:

❑ Day Use $ _____
❑ Camp Sites $_____
❑ RV Sites $ _____
❑ Refund policy

_____

_____

_____

Make It Personal

Trip dates:

Why I went:

I went with:

How I got there: (circle all that apply) Plane   Train   Car   Bus   Bike   Hike   RV   MC

We stayed in (space, cabin, etc.)

The weather was: Sunny   Cloudy   Rainy   Stormy   Snowy   Foggy   Warm   Cold

Most relaxing day:

Something funny:

Someone we met:

Best story told:

The kids liked this:

The best food:

Games played:

Something disappointing:

Next time I'll do this differently:

Don Pedro Island State Park
City: Cape Haze   County: Charlotte

Plan your trip https://www.floridastateparks.org/index.php/parks-and-trails/don-pedro-island-state-park

Activities:

- ❑ Birding / Wildlife
- ❑ Fishing
- ❑ Guided tours
- ❑ Geo cache
- ❑ Hiking
- ❑ Horseback
- ❑ Hunting
- ❑ Snorkeling
- ❑ Trails
- ❑ Water access

Facilities:

- ❑ ADA
- ❑ Meeting hall
- ❑ Pavilions
- ❑ Picnic sites
- ❑ Restrooms
- ❑ Visitor center
- ❑
- ❑
- ❑
- ❑

Get the Facts

- ❑ Phone 941-964-0375
- ❑ Park Hours

  _____

- ❑ Reservations? ____Y ____N

  date made_____

- ❑ Open year 'round ___Y___N

  dates_____

- ❑ Distance from home

  miles: _____

  hours: _____

- ❑ Address or GPS

  _____

  _____

Date visited:

I went with:
_____

My favorite things:
_____

_____

_____

Notes

Fees:

- ❑ Day Use $ _____
- ❑ Parking $_____
- ❑ Refund policy

  _____

  _____

Stump Pass Beach State Park
City: Englewood   County: Charlotte

Plan your trip https://www.floridastateparks.org/parks-and-trails/stump-pass-beach-state-park

Activities:

- ❑ Birding / Wildlife
- ❑ Fishing
- ❑ Guided tours
- ❑ Geo cache
- ❑ Hiking
- ❑ Horseback
- ❑ Hunting
- ❑ Snorkeling
- ❑ Trails
- ❑ Water access

Facilities:

- ❑ ADA
- ❑ Meeting hall
- ❑ Pavilions
- ❑ Picnic sites
- ❑ Restrooms
- ❑ Visitor center
- ❑
- ❑
- ❑
- ❑

Get the Facts

- ❑ Phone 941-964-0375
- ❑ Park Hours

    _____

- ❑ Reservations? ____Y ____N

    date made_____

- ❑ Open year 'round ___Y___N

    dates_____

- ❑ Distance from home

    miles: _____

    hours: _____

- ❑ Address or GPS

    _____

    _____

Date visited:

I went with:

_____

My favorite things:

_____

_____

_____

Notes

Fees:

- ❑ Day Use $ _____
- ❑ Parking $_____
- ❑ Refund policy

    _____

    _____

Charlotte Harbor Preserve SP
City: Punta Gorda   County: Charlotte / Lee

Plan your trip https://www.floridastateparks.org/parks-and-trails/charlotte-harbor-preserve-state-park

Activities:

- ❏ Birding / Wildlife
- ❏ Fishing
- ❏ Guided tours
- ❏ Geo cache
- ❏ Hiking
- ❏ Horseback
- ❏ Hunting
- ❏ Snorkeling
- ❏ Trails
- ❏ Water access

Facilities:

- ❏ ADA
- ❏ Meeting hall
- ❏ Pavilions
- ❏ Picnic sites
- ❏ Restrooms
- ❏ Visitor center
- ❏
- ❏
- ❏
- ❏

Get the Facts

- ❏ Phone 941-575-5816
- ❏ Park Hours

  _____

- ❏ Reservations? ____Y ____N

  date made_____

- ❏ Open year 'round ___Y___N

  dates_____

- ❏ Distance from home

  miles: _____

  hours: _____

- ❏ Address or GPS

  _____

  _____

Date visited:

I went with:
_____

My favorite things:
_____
_____
_____

Notes

Fees:

- ❏ Day Use $ _____
- ❏ Parking $_____
- ❏ Refund policy

  _____

  _____

226

Fakahatchee Strand Preserve SP
City: Copeland   County: Collier

Plan your trip https://www.floridastateparks.org/parks-and-trails/fakahatchee-strand-preserve-state-park

Activities:

❏ Birding / Wildlife
❏ Fishing
❏ Guided tours
❏ Geo cache
❏ Hiking
❏ Horseback
❏ Hunting
❏ Snorkeling
❏ Trails
❏ Water access

Facilities:

❏ ADA
❏ Meeting hall
❏ Pavilions
❏ Picnic sites
❏ Restrooms
❏ Visitor center
❏
❏
❏
❏

Get the Facts

❏ Phone 239-695-4593
❏ Park Hours

_____

❏ Reservations? ____Y ____N

date made_____

❏ Open year 'round ___Y___N

dates_____

❏ Distance from home

miles: _____

hours: _____

❏ Address or GPS

_____

_____

Date visited:

I went with:
_____

My favorite things:
_____

_____

_____

Notes

Fees:

❏ Day Use $ _____
❏ Parking $_____
❏ Refund policy

_____

_____

Delnor-Wiggins Pass State Park
City: Naples   County: Collier

Plan your trip https://www.floridastateparks.org/index.php/parks-and-trails/delnor-wiggins-pass-state-park

Activities:

- ❑ Birding / Wildlife
- ❑ Fishing
- ❑ Guided tours
- ❑ Geo cache
- ❑ Hiking
- ❑ Horseback
- ❑ Hunting
- ❑ Snorkeling
- ❑ Trails
- ❑ Water access

Facilities:

- ❑ ADA
- ❑ Meeting hall
- ❑ Pavilions
- ❑ Picnic sites
- ❑ Restrooms
- ❑ Visitor center
- ❑
- ❑
- ❑
- ❑

Get the Facts

- ❑ Phone 239-597-6196
- ❑ Park Hours

   _____

- ❑ Reservations? ____Y ____N

   date made_____

- ❑ Open year 'round ___Y___N

   dates_____

- ❑ Distance from home

   miles: _____

   hours: _____

- ❑ Address or GPS

   _____

   _____

Date visited:

I went with:
_____

My favorite things:
_____

_____

_____

Notes

Fees:

- ❑ Day Use $ _____
- ❑ Parking $_____
- ❑ Refund policy

   _____

   _____

Gasparilla Island State Park
City: Boca Grande   County: Lee

Plan your trip https://www.floridastateparks.org/index.php/parks-and-trails/gasparilla-island-state-park

Activities:

- ❑ Birding / Wildlife
- ❑ Fishing
- ❑ Guided tours
- ❑ Geo cache
- ❑ Hiking
- ❑ Horseback
- ❑ Hunting
- ❑ Snorkeling
- ❑ Trails
- ❑ Water access

Facilities:

- ❑ ADA
- ❑ Meeting hall
- ❑ Pavilions
- ❑ Picnic sites
- ❑ Restrooms
- ❑ Visitor center
- ❑
- ❑
- ❑
- ❑

Get the Facts

- ❑ Phone 941-964-0375
- ❑ Park Hours

  _____

- ❑ Reservations? ____Y ____N

  date made_____

- ❑ Open year 'round ___Y___N

  dates_____

- ❑ Distance from home

  miles: _____

  hours: _____

- ❑ Address or GPS

  _____

  _____

Date visited:

I went with: _____

My favorite things:
_____

_____

_____

Notes

Fees:

- ❑ Day Use $ _____
- ❑ Parking $_____
- ❑ Refund policy

  _____

  _____

Estero Bay Preserve State Park
City: Estero   County: Lee

Plan your trip https://www.floridastateparks.org/index.php/parks-and-trails/estero-bay-preserve-state-park

Activities:

- ❑ Birding / Wildlife
- ❑ Fishing
- ❑ Guided tours
- ❑ Geo cache
- ❑ Hiking
- ❑ Horseback
- ❑ Hunting
- ❑ Snorkeling
- ❑ Trails
- ❑ Water access

Facilities:

- ❑ ADA
- ❑ Meeting hall
- ❑ Pavilions
- ❑ Picnic sites
- ❑ Restrooms
- ❑ Visitor center
- ❑
- ❑
- ❑
- ❑

Get the Facts

- ❑ Phone 239-992-0311
- ❑ Park Hours

  _____

- ❑ Reservations? ____Y ____N

  date made_____

- ❑ Open year 'round ___Y___N

  dates_____

- ❑ Distance from home

  miles: _____

  hours: _____

- ❑ Address or GPS

  _____

  _____

Date visited:

I went with:
_____

My favorite things:
_____
_____
_____

Fees:

- ❑ Day Use $ _____
- ❑ Parking $_____
- ❑ Refund policy

  _____

  _____

Notes

Mound Key Archeological State Park
City: Estero
County: Lee

Plan your trip https://www.floridastateparks.org/parks-and-trails/mound-key-archaeological-state-park

Activities:

- ❑ Birding / Wildlife
- ❑ Fishing
- ❑ Guided tours
- ❑ Geo cache
- ❑ Hiking
- ❑ Horseback
- ❑ Hunting
- ❑ Snorkeling
- ❑ Trails
- ❑ Water access

Facilities:

- ❑ ADA
- ❑ Meeting hall
- ❑ Pavilions
- ❑ Picnic sites
- ❑ Restrooms
- ❑ Visitor center
- ❑
- ❑
- ❑
- ❑

Get the Facts

- ❑ Phone 239-992-0311
- ❑ Park Hours

  _____
- ❑ Reservations? ____Y ____N

  date made_____
- ❑ Open year 'round ___Y___N

  dates_____
- ❑ Distance from home

  miles: _____

  hours: _____
- ❑ Address or GPS

  _____

  _____

Date visited:

I went with:
_____

My favorite things:
_____
_____
_____

Notes

Fees:

- ❑ Day Use $ _____
- ❑ Parking $_____
- ❑ Refund policy

  _____

  _____

Lovers Key State Park
City: Fort Myers Beach   County: Lee

Plan your trip https://www.floridastateparks.org/parks-and-trails/lovers-key-state-park

Activities:

- ❑ Birding / Wildlife
- ❑ Fishing
- ❑ Guided tours
- ❑ Geo cache
- ❑ Hiking
- ❑ Horseback
- ❑ Hunting
- ❑ Snorkeling
- ❑ Trails
- ❑ Water access

Facilities:

- ❑ ADA
- ❑ Meeting hall
- ❑ Pavilions
- ❑ Picnic sites
- ❑ Restrooms
- ❑ Visitor center
- ❑
- ❑
- ❑
- ❑

Get the Facts

- ❑ Phone 239-463-4588
- ❑ Park Hours

    _____

- ❑ Reservations? ____Y ____N

    date made_____

- ❑ Open year 'round ___Y___N

    dates_____

- ❑ Distance from home

    miles: _____

    hours: _____

- ❑ Address or GPS

    _____

    _____

Date visited:

I went with:
_____

My favorite things:
_____

_____

_____

Fees:

- ❑ Day Use $ _____
- ❑ Parking $_____
- ❑ Refund policy

    _____

    _____

Notes

Southeast

- Broward
- Martin
- Miami-Dade
- Monroe
- Palm Beach

Hugh Taylor Birch State Park
City: Fort Lauderdale   County: Broward

Plan your Trip https://www.floridastateparks.org/HughTaylorBirch

Activities:

- ❑ Beach Access
- ❑ Biking Trails
- ❑ Boating
- ❑ Campfire
- ❑ Caving
- ❑ Disc Golf
- ❑ Fishing
- ❑ Geo Cache
- ❑ Golf
- ❑ Hiking
- ❑ Horseback

- ❑ Hunting
- ❑ OHV
- ❑ Park Tours
- ❑ Rock Climbing
- ❑ Snorkeling
- ❑ Stargazing
- ❑ Swimming
- ❑ Viewpoint
- ❑ Wildlife & Birding
- ❑
- ❑

Facilities:

- ❑ ADA
- ❑ Gym
- ❑ Historic Sites
- ❑ Lodge
- ❑ Meeting Hall
- ❑ Pavilions
- ❑ Picnic sites
- ❑ Pool
- ❑ Restrooms

- ❑ Showers
- ❑ Visitor Center
- ❑ RV Camp
- ❑ Tent Camp
- ❑ Cabins
- ❑ Lodge Rooms
- ❑
- ❑
- ❑

Notes:

Get the Facts

- ❑ Phone: 954-564-4521
- ❑ Park Hours

    _____

- ❑ Reservations? ____Y ____N

    date made_____

- ❑ Open year 'round ___Y___N

    dates_____

- ❑ Check in time _____
- ❑ Check out time _____
- ❑ Dog friendly _____Y _____N
- ❑ Max RV length _____
- ❑ Distance from home

    miles: _____

    hours: _____

- ❑ Address_____

    _____

    _____

Fees:

- ❑ Day Use $ _____
- ❑ Camp Sites $_____
- ❑ RV Sites $ _____
- ❑ Refund policy

    _____

    _____

    _____

Make It Personal

Trip dates:

Why I went:

I went with:

How I got there: (circle all that apply) Plane   Train   Car   Bus   Bike   Hike   RV   MC

We stayed in (space, cabin, etc.)

The weather was: Sunny   Cloudy   Rainy   Stormy   Snowy   Foggy   Warm   Cold

Most relaxing day:

Something funny:

Someone we met:

Best story told:

The kids liked this:

The best food:

Games played:

Something disappointing:

Next time I'll do this differently:

Jonathan Dickinson State Park
City: Hobe Sound   County: Martin

Plan your Trip https://www.floridastateparks.org/parks-and-trails/jonathan-dickinson-state-park

Activities:

- ❑ Beach Access
- ❑ Biking Trails
- ❑ Boating
- ❑ Campfire
- ❑ Caving
- ❑ Disc Golf
- ❑ Fishing
- ❑ Geo Cache
- ❑ Golf
- ❑ Hiking
- ❑ Horseback

- ❑ Hunting
- ❑ OHV
- ❑ Park Tours
- ❑ Rock Climbing
- ❑ Snorkeling
- ❑ Stargazing
- ❑ Swimming
- ❑ Viewpoint
- ❑ Wildlife & Birding
- ❑
- ❑

Facilities:

- ❑ ADA
- ❑ Gym
- ❑ Historic Sites
- ❑ Lodge
- ❑ Meeting Hall
- ❑ Pavilions
- ❑ Picnic sites
- ❑ Pool
- ❑ Restrooms

- ❑ Showers
- ❑ Visitor Center
- ❑ RV Camp
- ❑ Tent Camp
- ❑ Cabins
- ❑ Lodge Rooms
- ❑
- ❑
- ❑

Notes:

Get the Facts

- ❑ Phone: 772-546-2771
- ❑ Park Hours

  _____

- ❑ Reservations? ____Y ____N

  date made_____

- ❑ Open year 'round ___Y___N

  dates_____

- ❑ Check in time _____
- ❑ Check out time _____
- ❑ Dog friendly _____Y _____N
- ❑ Max RV length _____
- ❑ Distance from home

  miles: _____

  hours: _____

- ❑ Address_____

  _____

  _____

Fees:

- ❑ Day Use $ _____
- ❑ Camp Sites $_____
- ❑ RV Sites $ _____
- ❑ Refund policy

  _____

  _____

  _____

Make It Personal

Trip dates:

Why I went:

I went with:

How I got there: (circle all that apply) Plane   Train   Car   Bus   Bike   Hike   RV   MC

We stayed in (space, cabin, etc.)

The weather was: Sunny Cloudy Rainy Stormy Snowy Foggy Warm Cold

Most relaxing day:

Something funny:

Someone we met:

Best story told:

The kids liked this:

The best food:

Games played:

Something disappointing:

Next time I'll do this differently:

Bill Baggs Cape Florida State Park
City: Key Biscayne   County: Miami-Dade

Plan your Trip https://www.floridastateparks.org/index.php/parks-and-trails/bill-baggs-cape-florida-state-park

Activities:

- ❑ Beach Access
- ❑ Biking Trails
- ❑ Boating
- ❑ Campfire
- ❑ Caving
- ❑ Disc Golf
- ❑ Fishing
- ❑ Geo Cache
- ❑ Golf
- ❑ Hiking
- ❑ Horseback

- ❑ Hunting
- ❑ OHV
- ❑ Park Tours
- ❑ Rock Climbing
- ❑ Snorkeling
- ❑ Stargazing
- ❑ Swimming
- ❑ Viewpoint
- ❑ Wildlife & Birding
- ❑
- ❑

Facilities:

- ❑ ADA
- ❑ Gym
- ❑ Historic Sites
- ❑ Lodge
- ❑ Meeting Hall
- ❑ Pavilions
- ❑ Picnic sites
- ❑ Pool
- ❑ Restrooms

- ❑ Showers
- ❑ Visitor Center
- ❑ RV Camp
- ❑ Tent Camp
- ❑ Cabins
- ❑ Lodge Rooms
- ❑
- ❑
- ❑

Notes:

Get the Facts

- ❑ Phone: 786-582-2673
- ❑ Park Hours

  _____

- ❑ Reservations? ____Y ____N

  date made_____

- ❑ Open year 'round ___Y___N

  dates_____

- ❑ Check in time _____
- ❑ Check out time _____
- ❑ Dog friendly _____Y _____N
- ❑ Max RV length _____
- ❑ Distance from home

  miles: _____

  hours: _____

- ❑ Address_____

  _____

  _____

Fees:

- ❑ Day Use $ _____
- ❑ Camp Sites $_____
- ❑ RV Sites $ _____
- ❑ Refund policy

  _____

  _____

  _____

Make It Personal

Trip dates: _____

Why I went: _____

I went with: _____

How I got there: (circle all that apply) Plane   Train   Car   Bus   Bike   Hike   RV   MC

We stayed in (space, cabin, etc.) _____

_____

The weather was: Sunny   Cloudy   Rainy   Stormy   Snowy   Foggy   Warm   Cold

Most relaxing day: _____

_____

Something funny: _____

_____

Someone we met: _____

_____

Best story told: _____

_____

The kids liked this: _____

The best food: _____

Games played: _____

Something disappointing: _____

Next time I'll do this differently: _____

Oleta River State Park
City: North Miami Beach   County: Miami-Dade

Plan your Trip https://www.floridastateparks.org/OletaRiver

Activities:

- ❑ Beach Access
- ❑ Biking Trails
- ❑ Boating
- ❑ Campfire
- ❑ Caving
- ❑ Disc Golf
- ❑ Fishing
- ❑ Geo Cache
- ❑ Golf
- ❑ Hiking
- ❑ Horseback
- ❑ Hunting
- ❑ OHV
- ❑ Park Tours
- ❑ Rock Climbing
- ❑ Snorkeling
- ❑ Stargazing
- ❑ Swimming
- ❑ Viewpoint
- ❑ Wildlife & Birding
- ❑
- ❑

Facilities:

- ❑ ADA
- ❑ Gym
- ❑ Historic Sites
- ❑ Lodge
- ❑ Meeting Hall
- ❑ Pavilions
- ❑ Picnic sites
- ❑ Pool
- ❑ Restrooms
- ❑ Showers
- ❑ Visitor Center
- ❑ RV Camp
- ❑ Tent Camp
- ❑ Cabins
- ❑ Lodge Rooms
- ❑
- ❑
- ❑

Notes:

Get the Facts

- ❑ Phone: 305-919-1846
- ❑ Park Hours

  _____
- ❑ Reservations? ____Y ____N

  date made_____
- ❑ Open year 'round ___Y___N

  dates_____
- ❑ Check in time _____
- ❑ Check out time _____
- ❑ Dog friendly _____Y _____N
- ❑ Max RV length _____
- ❑ Distance from home

  miles: _____

  hours: _____
- ❑ Address_____

  _____

  _____

Fees:

- ❑ Day Use $ _____
- ❑ Camp Sites $_____
- ❑ RV Sites $ _____
- ❑ Refund policy

  _____

  _____

  _____

Make It Personal

Trip dates:

Why I went:

I went with:

How I got there: (circle all that apply) Plane   Train   Car   Bus   Bike   Hike   RV   MC

We stayed in (space, cabin, etc.)

The weather was: Sunny   Cloudy   Rainy   Stormy   Snowy   Foggy   Warm   Cold

Most relaxing day:

Something funny:

Someone we met:

Best story told:

The kids liked this:

The best food:

Games played:

Something disappointing:

Next time I'll do this differently:

Bahia Honda State Park
City: Big Pine Key   County: Monroe

Plan your Trip https://www.floridastateparks.org/BahiaHonda

Activities:

- ❑ Beach Access
- ❑ Biking Trails
- ❑ Boating
- ❑ Campfire
- ❑ Caving
- ❑ Disc Golf
- ❑ Fishing
- ❑ Geo Cache
- ❑ Golf
- ❑ Hiking
- ❑ Horseback

- ❑ Hunting
- ❑ OHV
- ❑ Park Tours
- ❑ Rock Climbing
- ❑ Snorkeling
- ❑ Stargazing
- ❑ Swimming
- ❑ Viewpoint
- ❑ Wildlife & Birding
- ❑
- ❑

Facilities:

- ❑ ADA
- ❑ Gym
- ❑ Historic Sites
- ❑ Lodge
- ❑ Meeting Hall
- ❑ Pavilions
- ❑ Picnic sites
- ❑ Pool
- ❑ Restrooms

- ❑ Showers
- ❑ Visitor Center
- ❑ RV Camp
- ❑ Tent Camp
- ❑ Cabins
- ❑ Lodge Rooms
- ❑
- ❑
- ❑

Notes:

Get the Facts

- ❑ Phone: 305-872-2353
- ❑ Park Hours

  _____

- ❑ Reservations? ____Y ____N

  date made_____

- ❑ Open year 'round ___Y___N

  dates_____

- ❑ Check in time _____
- ❑ Check out time _____
- ❑ Dog friendly _____Y _____N
- ❑ Max RV length _____
- ❑ Distance from home

  miles: _____

  hours: _____

- ❑ Address_____

  _____

  _____

Fees:

- ❑ Day Use $ _____
- ❑ Camp Sites $_____
- ❑ RV Sites $ _____
- ❑ Refund policy

  _____

  _____

  _____

Make It Personal

Trip dates:

Why I went:

I went with:

How I got there: (circle all that apply) Plane   Train   Car   Bus   Bike   Hike   RV   MC

We stayed in (space, cabin, etc.)

The weather was: Sunny   Cloudy   Rainy   Stormy   Snowy   Foggy   Warm   Cold

Most relaxing day:

Something funny:

Someone we met:

Best story told:

The kids liked this:

The best food:

Games played:

Something disappointing:

Next time I'll do this differently:

John Pennekamp Coral Reef SP

City: Key Largo   **County: Monroe**

Plan your Trip https://www.floridastateparks.org/parks-and-trails/john-pennekamp-coral-reef-state-park

Activities:

- ❑ Beach Access
- ❑ Biking Trails
- ❑ Boating
- ❑ Campfire
- ❑ Caving
- ❑ Disc Golf
- ❑ Fishing
- ❑ Geo Cache
- ❑ Golf
- ❑ Hiking
- ❑ Horseback

- ❑ Hunting
- ❑ OHV
- ❑ Park Tours
- ❑ Rock Climbing
- ❑ Snorkeling
- ❑ Stargazing
- ❑ Swimming
- ❑ Viewpoint
- ❑ Wildlife & Birding
- ❑
- ❑

Facilities:

- ❑ ADA
- ❑ Gym
- ❑ Historic Sites
- ❑ Lodge
- ❑ Meeting Hall
- ❑ Pavilions
- ❑ Picnic sites
- ❑ Pool
- ❑ Restrooms

- ❑ Showers
- ❑ Visitor Center
- ❑ RV Camp
- ❑ Tent Camp
- ❑ Cabins
- ❑ Lodge Rooms
- ❑
- ❑
- ❑

Notes:

Get the Facts

- ❑ Phone: 305-676-3777
- ❑ Park Hours

  _____

- ❑ Reservations? ____Y ____N

  date made_____

- ❑ Open year 'round ___Y___N

  dates_____

- ❑ Check in time _____
- ❑ Check out time _____
- ❑ Dog friendly _____Y _____N
- ❑ Max RV length _____
- ❑ Distance from home

  miles: _____

  hours: _____

- ❑ Address_____

  _____

  _____

Fees:

- ❑ Day Use $ _____
- ❑ Camp Sites $_____
- ❑ RV Sites $ _____
- ❑ Refund policy

  _____

  _____

  _____

Make It Personal

Trip dates:

Why I went:

I went with:

How I got there: (circle all that apply) Plane   Train   Car   Bus   Bike   Hike   RV   MC

We stayed in (space, cabin, etc.)

The weather was: Sunny   Cloudy   Rainy   Stormy   Snowy   Foggy   Warm   Cold

Most relaxing day:

Something funny:

Someone we met:

Best story told:

The kids liked this:

The best food:

Games played:

Something disappointing:

Next time I'll do this differently:

245

Long Key State Park
City: Long Key   County: Monroe

Plan your Trip https://www.floridastateparks.org/parks-and-trails/long-key-state-park

Activities:

- ❏ Beach Access
- ❏ Biking Trails
- ❏ Boating
- ❏ Campfire
- ❏ Caving
- ❏ Disc Golf
- ❏ Fishing
- ❏ Geo Cache
- ❏ Golf
- ❏ Hiking
- ❏ Horseback

- ❏ Hunting
- ❏ OHV
- ❏ Park Tours
- ❏ Rock Climbing
- ❏ Snorkeling
- ❏ Stargazing
- ❏ Swimming
- ❏ Viewpoint
- ❏ Wildlife & Birding
- ❏
- ❏

Facilities:

- ❏ ADA
- ❏ Gym
- ❏ Historic Sites
- ❏ Lodge
- ❏ Meeting Hall
- ❏ Pavilions
- ❏ Picnic sites
- ❏ Pool
- ❏ Restrooms

- ❏ Showers
- ❏ Visitor Center
- ❏ RV Camp
- ❏ Tent Camp
- ❏ Cabins
- ❏ Lodge Rooms
- ❏
- ❏
- ❏

Notes:

Get the Facts

- ❏ Phone: 305-664-4815
- ❏ Park Hours

  _____

- ❏ Reservations? ____Y ____N

  date made_____

- ❏ Open year 'round ___Y___N

  dates_____

- ❏ Check in time _____
- ❏ Check out time _____
- ❏ Dog friendly _____Y _____N
- ❏ Max RV length _____
- ❏ Distance from home

  miles: _____

  hours: _____

- ❏ Address_____

  _____

  _____

Fees:

- ❏ Day Use $ _____
- ❏ Camp Sites $_____
- ❏ RV Sites $ _____
- ❏ Refund policy

  _____

  _____

  _____

Make It Personal

Trip dates:

Why I went:

I went with:

How I got there: (circle all that apply) Plane   Train   Car   Bus   Bike   Hike   RV   MC

We stayed in (space, cabin, etc.)

The weather was: Sunny   Cloudy   Rainy   Stormy   Snowy   Foggy   Warm   Cold

Most relaxing day:

Something funny:

Someone we met:

Best story told:

The kids liked this:

The best food:

Games played:

Something disappointing:

Next time I'll do this differently:

Curry Hammock State Park
City: Marathon   County: Monroe

Plan your Trip https://www.floridastateparks.org/parks-and-trails/curry-hammock-state-park

Activities:

- ❑ Beach Access
- ❑ Biking Trails
- ❑ Boating
- ❑ Campfire
- ❑ Caving
- ❑ Disc Golf
- ❑ Fishing
- ❑ Geo Cache
- ❑ Golf
- ❑ Hiking
- ❑ Horseback

- ❑ Hunting
- ❑ OHV
- ❑ Park Tours
- ❑ Rock Climbing
- ❑ Snorkeling
- ❑ Stargazing
- ❑ Swimming
- ❑ Viewpoint
- ❑ Wildlife & Birding
- ❑
- ❑

Facilities:

- ❑ ADA
- ❑ Gym
- ❑ Historic Sites
- ❑ Lodge
- ❑ Meeting Hall
- ❑ Pavilions
- ❑ Picnic sites
- ❑ Pool
- ❑ Restrooms

- ❑ Showers
- ❑ Visitor Center
- ❑ RV Camp
- ❑ Tent Camp
- ❑ Cabins
- ❑ Lodge Rooms
- ❑
- ❑
- ❑

Notes:

Get the Facts

- ❑ Phone: 305-289-2690
- ❑ Park Hours

  _____

- ❑ Reservations? ____Y ____N

  date made_____

- ❑ Open year 'round ___Y___N

  dates_____

- ❑ Check in time _____
- ❑ Check out time _____
- ❑ Dog friendly _____Y _____N
- ❑ Max RV length _____
- ❑ Distance from home

  miles: _____

  hours: _____

- ❑ Address_____

  _____

  _____

Fees:

- ❑ Day Use $ _____
- ❑ Camp Sites $_____
- ❑ RV Sites $ _____
- ❑ Refund policy

  _____

  _____

  _____

Make It Personal

Trip dates: _____

Why I went: _____

I went with: _____

How I got there: (circle all that apply) Plane   Train   Car   Bus   Bike   Hike   RV   MC

We stayed in (space, cabin, etc.) _____

_____

The weather was: Sunny   Cloudy   Rainy   Stormy   Snowy   Foggy   Warm   Cold

Most relaxing day: _____

_____

Something funny: _____

_____

Someone we met: _____

_____

Best story told: _____

_____

The kids liked this: _____

The best food: _____

_____

Games played: _____

_____

Something disappointing: _____

_____

Next time I'll do this differently: _____

_____

Dr. Von D. Mizell-Eula Johnson SP
City: Dania Beach   County: Broward

Plan your trip https://www.floridastateparks.org/index.php/mizell

Activities:

- ❑ Birding / Wildlife
- ❑ Fishing
- ❑ Guided tours
- ❑ Geo cache
- ❑ Hiking
- ❑ Horseback
- ❑ Hunting
- ❑ Snorkeling
- ❑ Trails
- ❑ Water access

Facilities:

- ❑ ADA
- ❑ Meeting hall
- ❑ Pavilions
- ❑ Picnic sites
- ❑ Restrooms
- ❑ Visitor center
- ❑
- ❑
- ❑
- ❑

Get the Facts

- ❑ Phone 954-923-2833
- ❑ Park Hours

  _____

- ❑ Reservations? ____Y ____N

  date made_____

- ❑ Open year 'round ___Y___N

  dates_____

- ❑ Distance from home

  miles: _____

  hours: _____

- ❑ Address or GPS

  _____

  _____

Date visited:

I went with:
_____

My favorite things:
_____

_____

_____

Notes

Fees:

- ❑ Day Use $ _____
- ❑ Parking $_____
- ❑ Refund policy

  _____

  _____

St. Lucie Inlet Preserve State Park
City: Port Salerno   County: Martin

Plan your trip https://www.floridastateparks.org/parks-and-trails/st-lucie-inlet-preserve-state-park

Activities:

- ❑ Birding / Wildlife
- ❑ Fishing
- ❑ Guided tours
- ❑ Geo cache
- ❑ Hiking
- ❑ Horseback
- ❑ Hunting
- ❑ Snorkeling
- ❑ Trails
- ❑ Water access

Facilities:

- ❑ ADA
- ❑ Meeting hall
- ❑ Pavilions
- ❑ Picnic sites
- ❑ Restrooms
- ❑ Visitor center
- ❑
- ❑
- ❑
- ❑

Get the Facts

- ❑ Phone 772-219-1880
- ❑ Park Hours

  _____

- ❑ Reservations? _____Y _____N

  date made_____

- ❑ Open year 'round ___Y___N

  dates_____

- ❑ Distance from home

  miles: _____

  hours: _____

- ❑ Address or GPS

  _____

  _____

Date visited:

I went with:

_____

My favorite things:

_____

_____

_____

Notes

Fees:

- ❑ Day Use $ _____
- ❑ Parking $_____
- ❑ Refund policy

  _____

  _____

Seabranch Preserve State Park
City: Stuart   County: Martin

Plan your trip https://www.floridastateparks.org/parks-and-trails/seabranch-preserve-state-park

Activities:

- ❏ Birding / Wildlife
- ❏ Fishing
- ❏ Guided tours
- ❏ Geo cache
- ❏ Hiking
- ❏ Horseback
- ❏ Hunting
- ❏ Snorkeling
- ❏ Trails
- ❏ Water access

Facilities:

- ❏ ADA
- ❏ Meeting hall
- ❏ Pavilions
- ❏ Picnic sites
- ❏ Restrooms
- ❏ Visitor center
- ❏
- ❏
- ❏
- ❏

Get the Facts

- ❏ Phone 772-219-1880
- ❏ Park Hours

  _____

- ❏ Reservations? ____Y ____N

  date made_____

- ❏ Open year 'round ___Y___N

  dates_____

- ❏ Distance from home

  miles: _____

  hours: _____

- ❏ Address or GPS

  _____

  _____

Date visited:

I went with:
_____

My favorite things:
_____

_____

_____

Notes

Fees:

- ❏ Day Use $ _____
- ❏ Parking $_____
- ❏ Refund policy

  _____

  _____

The Barnacle Historic State Park

City: Miami   **County: Miami-Dade**

Plan your trip https://www.floridastateparks.org/parks-and-trails/barnacle-historic-state-park

Activities:

- ❑ Birding / Wildlife
- ❑ Fishing
- ❑ Guided tours
- ❑ Geo cache
- ❑ Hiking
- ❑ Horseback
- ❑ Hunting
- ❑ Snorkeling
- ❑ Trails
- ❑ Water access

Facilities:

- ❑ ADA
- ❑ Meeting hall
- ❑ Pavilions
- ❑ Picnic sites
- ❑ Restrooms
- ❑ Visitor center
- ❑
- ❑
- ❑
- ❑

Get the Facts

- ❑ Phone 305-442-6866
- ❑ Park Hours

  _____

- ❑ Reservations? ____Y ____N

  date made_____

- ❑ Open year 'round ___Y___N

  dates_____

- ❑ Distance from home

  miles: _____

  hours: _____

- ❑ Address or GPS

  _____

  _____

Date visited:

I went with:
_____

My favorite things:
_____

_____

_____

Notes

Fees:

- ❑ Day Use $ _____
- ❑ Parking $_____
- ❑ Refund policy

  _____

  _____

Bald Point State Park
City: Alligator Point   County: Monroe

Plan your trip https://www.floridastateparks.org/index.php/parks-and-trails/bald-point-state-park

Activities:

- ❑ Birding / Wildlife
- ❑ Fishing
- ❑ Guided tours
- ❑ Geo cache
- ❑ Hiking
- ❑ Horseback
- ❑ Hunting
- ❑ Snorkeling
- ❑ Trails
- ❑ Water access

Facilities:

- ❑ ADA
- ❑ Meeting hall
- ❑ Pavilions
- ❑ Picnic sites
- ❑ Restrooms
- ❑ Visitor center
- ❑
- ❑
- ❑
- ❑

Get the Facts

- ❑ Phone 850-349-9146
- ❑ Park Hours

   _____

- ❑ Reservations? ____Y ____N

   date made_____

- ❑ Open year 'round ___Y___N

   dates_____

- ❑ Distance from home

   miles: _____

   hours: _____

- ❑ Address or GPS

   _____

   _____

Date visited:

I went with:

_____

My favorite things:

_____

_____

_____

Notes

Fees:

- ❑ Day Use $ _____
- ❑ Parking $_____
- ❑ Refund policy

   _____

   _____

Indian Key Historic State Park
City: Islamorada   County: Monroe

Plan your trip https://www.floridastateparks.org/IndianKey

Activities:

- ❏ Birding / Wildlife
- ❏ Fishing
- ❏ Guided tours
- ❏ Geo cache
- ❏ Hiking
- ❏ Horseback
- ❏ Hunting
- ❏ Snorkeling
- ❏ Trails
- ❏ Water access

Facilities:

- ❏ ADA
- ❏ Meeting hall
- ❏ Pavilions
- ❏ Picnic sites
- ❏ Restrooms
- ❏ Visitor center
- ❏
- ❏
- ❏
- ❏

Get the Facts

- ❏ Phone 305-664-2540
- ❏ Park Hours

  _____

- ❏ Reservations? ____Y ____N

  date made_____

- ❏ Open year 'round ___Y___N

  dates_____

- ❏ Distance from home

  miles: _____

  hours: _____

- ❏ Address or GPS

  _____

  _____

Date visited:

I went with:

_____

My favorite things:

_____

_____

_____

Notes

Fees:

- ❏ Day Use $ _____
- ❏ Parking $_____
- ❏ Refund policy

  _____

  _____

Lignumvitae Key Botanical State Park
City: Islamorada   County: Monroe

Plan your trip https://www.floridastateparks.org/LignumvitaeKey

Activities:

- ❑ Birding / Wildlife
- ❑ Fishing
- ❑ Guided tours
- ❑ Geo cache
- ❑ Hiking
- ❑ Horseback
- ❑ Hunting
- ❑ Snorkeling
- ❑ Trails
- ❑ Water access

Facilities:

- ❑ ADA
- ❑ Meeting hall
- ❑ Pavilions
- ❑ Picnic sites
- ❑ Restrooms
- ❑ Visitor center
- ❑
- ❑
- ❑
- ❑

Get the Facts

- ❑ Phone 305-664-2540
- ❑ Park Hours

  _____

- ❑ Reservations? ____Y ____N

  date made_____

- ❑ Open year 'round ___Y___N

  dates_____

- ❑ Distance from home

  miles: _____

  hours: _____

- ❑ Address or GPS

  _____

  _____

Date visited:

I went with:
_____

My favorite things:
_____

_____

_____

Notes

Fees:

- ❑ Day Use $ _____
- ❑ Parking $_____
- ❑ Refund policy

  _____

  _____

San Pedro Underwater Archaeological Preserve SP

City: Islamorada   County: Monroe

Plan your trip https://www.floridastateparks.org/SanPedro

Activities:

- ❑ Birding / Wildlife
- ❑ Fishing
- ❑ Guided tours
- ❑ Geo cache
- ❑ Hiking
- ❑ Horseback
- ❑ Hunting
- ❑ Snorkeling
- ❑ Trails
- ❑ Water access

Facilities:

- ❑ ADA
- ❑ Meeting hall
- ❑ Pavilions
- ❑ Picnic sites
- ❑ Restrooms
- ❑ Visitor center
- ❑
- ❑
- ❑
- ❑

Get the Facts

- ❑ Phone 305-664-2540
- ❑ Park Hours

  _____

- ❑ Reservations? ____Y ____N

  date made_____

- ❑ Open year 'round ___Y___N

  dates_____

- ❑ Distance from home

  miles: _____

  hours: _____

- ❑ Address or GPS

  _____

  _____

Date visited:

I went with:

_____

My favorite things:

_____

_____

_____

Notes

Fees:

- ❑ Day Use $ _____
- ❑ Parking $_____
- ❑ Refund policy

  _____

  _____

Windley Key Fossil Reef Geological SP
City: Islamorada   County: Monroe

Plan your trip https://www.floridastateparks.org/WindleyKey

Activities:

- ❑ Birding / Wildlife
- ❑ Fishing
- ❑ Guided tours
- ❑ Geo cache
- ❑ Hiking
- ❑ Horseback
- ❑ Hunting
- ❑ Snorkeling
- ❑ Trails
- ❑ Water access

Facilities:

- ❑ ADA
- ❑ Meeting hall
- ❑ Pavilions
- ❑ Picnic sites
- ❑ Restrooms
- ❑ Visitor center
- ❑
- ❑
- ❑
- ❑

Get the Facts

- ❑ Phone 305-664-2540
- ❑ Park Hours

_____

- ❑ Reservations? ____Y ____N

date made_____

- ❑ Open year 'round ___Y___N

dates_____

- ❑ Distance from home

miles: _____

hours: _____

- ❑ Address or GPS

_____

_____

Date visited:

I went with:

_____

My favorite things:

_____

_____

_____

Notes

Fees:

- ❑ Day Use $ _____
- ❑ Parking $_____
- ❑ Refund policy

_____

_____

Dagny Johnson Key Largo Hammock Botanical SP
City: Key Largo   County: Monroe

Plan your trip https://www.floridastateparks.org/index.php/parks-and-trails/dagny-johnson-key-largo-hammock-botanical-state-park

Activities:

- ❏ Birding / Wildlife
- ❏ Fishing
- ❏ Guided tours
- ❏ Geo cache
- ❏ Hiking
- ❏ Horseback
- ❏ Hunting
- ❏ Snorkeling
- ❏ Trails
- ❏ Water access

Facilities:

- ❏ ADA
- ❏ Meeting hall
- ❏ Pavilions
- ❏ Picnic sites
- ❏ Restrooms
- ❏ Visitor center
- ❏
- ❏
- ❏
- ❏

Get the Facts

- ❏ Phone 305-676-3777
- ❏ Park Hours

  _____

- ❏ Reservations? ____Y ____N

  date made_____

- ❏ Open year 'round ___Y___N

  dates_____

- ❏ Distance from home

  miles: _____

  hours: _____

- ❏ Address or GPS

  _____

  _____

Date visited:

I went with:

_____

My favorite things:

_____

_____

_____

Notes

Fees:

- ❏ Day Use $ _____
- ❏ Parking $_____
- ❏ Refund policy

  _____

  _____

Fort Zachary Taylor Historic SP
City: Key West   County: Monroe

Plan your trip https://www.floridastateparks.org/parks-and-trails/fort-zachary-taylor-historic-state-park

Activities:
- ❏ Birding / Wildlife
- ❏ Fishing
- ❏ Guided tours
- ❏ Geo cache
- ❏ Hiking
- ❏ Horseback
- ❏ Hunting
- ❏ Snorkeling
- ❏ Trails
- ❏ Water access

Facilities:
- ❏ ADA
- ❏ Meeting hall
- ❏ Pavilions
- ❏ Picnic sites
- ❏ Restrooms
- ❏ Visitor center
- ❏
- ❏
- ❏
- ❏

Get the Facts
- ❏ Phone 305-292-6713
- ❏ Park Hours

  _____

- ❏ Reservations? ____Y ____N

  date made_____

- ❏ Open year 'round ___Y___N

  dates_____

- ❏ Distance from home

  miles: _____

  hours: _____

- ❏ Address or GPS

  _____

  _____

Date visited:

I went with:

_____

My favorite things:

_____

_____

_____

Notes

Fees:
- ❏ Day Use $ _____
- ❏ Parking $_____
- ❏ Refund policy

  _____

  _____

John D. MacArthur Beach State Park
City: North Palm Beach   County: Palm Beach

Plan your trip https://www.floridastateparks.org/index.php/parks-and-trails/john-d-macarthur-beach-state-park

Activities:

- ❑ Birding / Wildlife
- ❑ Fishing
- ❑ Guided tours
- ❑ Geo cache
- ❑ Hiking
- ❑ Horseback
- ❑ Hunting
- ❑ Snorkeling
- ❑ Trails
- ❑ Water access

Facilities:

- ❑ ADA
- ❑ Meeting hall
- ❑ Pavilions
- ❑ Picnic sites
- ❑ Restrooms
- ❑ Visitor center
- ❑
- ❑
- ❑
- ❑

Get the Facts

- ❑ Phone 561-624-6950
- ❑ Park Hours

    _____

- ❑ Reservations? ____Y ____N

    date made_____

- ❑ Open year 'round ___Y___N

    dates_____

- ❑ Distance from home

    miles: _____

    hours: _____

- ❑ Address or GPS

    _____

    _____

Date visited:

I went with:

_____

My favorite things:

_____

_____

_____

Notes

Fees:

- ❑ Day Use $ _____
- ❑ Parking $_____
- ❑ Refund policy

    _____

    _____

Trails

- Alachua
- Citrus
- Clay
- Gilchrist
- Lafayette
- Marion
- Monroe
- Polk
- Santa Rosa
- St. Johns
- Wakulla

Suwannee River Wilderness State Trailhead

City: Mayo   County: Lafayette

Plan your trip https://www.floridastateparks.org/parks-and-trails/suwannee-river-wilderness-state-trail

Activities:

- ❑ Biking / Mountain
- ❑ Birding
- ❑ Boating
- ❑ Fishing
- ❑ Geo-Seeking
- ❑ Hiking
- ❑ Horseback Riding
- ❑ Paddling
- ❑ Picnicking
- ❑ Roller Blading
- ❑ Wildlife viewing

Facilities:

- ❑ ADA
- ❑ Camping
- ❑ Equestrian Camping
- ❑ Pavilions
- ❑ Picnic sites
- ❑ Playground
- ❑ Restrooms
- ❑
- ❑
- ❑

Get the Facts

- ❑ Phone   800-868-9914
- ❑ Park Hours

   _____

- ❑ Reservations? ____Y ____N

   date made_____

- ❑ Open year 'round ___Y___N

   dates_____

- ❑ Distance from home

   miles: _____

   hours: _____

- ❑ Address or GPS

   _____

   _____

Date visited:

I went with:

_____

My favorite things:

_____

_____

_____

Notes

Fees:

- ❑ Day Use $ _____
- ❑ Parking $_____
- ❑ Refund policy

   _____

   _____

Ross Prairie Trailhead & Campground
City: Dunnellon   County: Marion

Plan your trip https://www.floridastateparks.org/parks-and-trails/ross-prairie-trailhead-campground

Activities:

- ❑ Biking / Mountain
- ❑ Birding
- ❑ Boating
- ❑ Fishing
- ❑ Geo-Seeking
- ❑ Hiking
- ❑ Horseback Riding
- ❑ Paddling
- ❑ Picnicking
- ❑ Roller Blading
- ❑ Wildlife viewing

Facilities:

- ❑ ADA
- ❑ Camping
- ❑ Equestrian Camping
- ❑ Pavilions
- ❑ Picnic sites
- ❑ Playground
- ❑ Restrooms
- ❑
- ❑
- ❑

Get the Facts

- ❑ Phone   352-732-2606
- ❑ Park Hours

  _____

- ❑ Reservations? ____Y ____N

  date made_____

- ❑ Open year 'round ___Y___N

  dates_____

- ❑ Distance from home

  miles: _____

  hours: _____

- ❑ Address or GPS

  _____

  _____

Date visited:

I went with:

_____

My favorite things:

_____

_____

_____

Notes

Fees:

- ❑ Day Use $ _____
- ❑ Parking $_____
- ❑ Refund policy

  _____

  _____

Santos Trailhead & Campground
City: Ocala   County: Marion

Plan your trip https://www.floridastateparks.org/parks-and-trails/santos-trailhead-campground

Activities:

- ❏ Biking / Mountain
- ❏ Birding
- ❏ Boating
- ❏ Fishing
- ❏ Geo-Seeking
- ❏ Hiking
- ❏ Horseback Riding
- ❏ Paddling
- ❏ Picnicking
- ❏ Roller Blading
- ❏ Wildlife viewing

Facilities:

- ❏ ADA
- ❏ Camping
- ❏ Equestrian Camping
- ❏ Pavilions
- ❏ Picnic sites
- ❏ Playground
- ❏ Restrooms
- ❏
- ❏
- ❏

Get the Facts

- ❏ Phone   352-369-2693
- ❏ Park Hours

_____

- ❏ Reservations? ____Y ____N

  date made_____

- ❏ Open year 'round ___Y___N

  dates_____

- ❏ Distance from home

  miles: _____

  hours: _____

- ❏ Address or GPS

_____

_____

Fees:

- ❏ Day Use $ _____
- ❏ Parking $_____
- ❏ Refund policy

_____

_____

Date visited:

I went with:

_____

My favorite things:

_____

_____

_____

Notes

Shangri-La Trailhead & Campground
City: Ocala   County: Marion

Plan your trip https://www.floridastateparks.org/index.php/parks-and-trails/shangri-la-trailhead-campground

Activities:

- ❏ Biking / Mountain
- ❏ Birding
- ❏ Boating
- ❏ Fishing
- ❏ Geo-Seeking
- ❏ Hiking
- ❏ Horseback Riding
- ❏ Paddling
- ❏ Picnicking
- ❏ Roller Blading
- ❏ Wildlife viewing

Facilities:

- ❏ ADA
- ❏ Camping
- ❏ Equestrian Camping
- ❏ Pavilions
- ❏ Picnic sites
- ❏ Playground
- ❏ Restrooms
- ❏
- ❏
- ❏

Get the Facts

- ❏ Phone   352-347-1163
- ❏ Park Hours

  _____

- ❏ Reservations? ____ Y ____ N

  date made_____

- ❏ Open year 'round ___ Y ___ N

  dates_____

- ❏ Distance from home

  miles: _____

  hours: _____

- ❏ Address or GPS

  _____

  _____

Date visited:

I went with:
_____

My favorite things:
_____

_____

_____

Notes

Fees:

- ❏ Day Use $ _____
- ❏ Parking $_____
- ❏ Refund policy

  _____

  _____

Blackwater Heritage Trail
City: Milton   County: Santa Rosa

Plan your trip https://www.floridastateparks.org/parks-and-trails/blackwater-heritage-state-trail

Activities:

- ❑ Biking / Mountain
- ❑ Birding
- ❑ Boating
- ❑ Fishing
- ❑ Geo-Seeking
- ❑ Hiking
- ❑ Horseback Riding
- ❑ Paddling
- ❑ Picnicking
- ❑ Roller Blading
- ❑ Wildlife viewing

Facilities:

- ❑ ADA
- ❑ Pavilions
- ❑ Picnic sites
- ❑ Playground
- ❑ Restrooms
- ❑ Visitor center
- ❑
- ❑
- ❑
- ❑
- ❑

Get the Facts

- ❑ Phone   850-983-5338
- ❑ Park Hours

_____

- ❑ Distance from home

  miles: _____

  hours: _____

- ❑ Address or GPS

_____

_____

Date visited:

I went with:

_____

My favorite things:

_____

_____

_____

Fees:

- ❑ Day Use $ _____
- ❑ Parking $_____
- ❑ Refund policy

_____

_____

Notes

Gainesville-Hawthorne State Trail
City: Gainesville   County: Alachua

Plan your trip https://www.floridastateparks.org/parks-and-trails/gainesville-hawthorne-state-trail

Activities:

- ❑ Biking / Mountain
- ❑ Birding
- ❑ Boating
- ❑ Fishing
- ❑ Geo-Seeking
- ❑ Hiking
- ❑ Horseback Riding
- ❑ Paddling
- ❑ Picnicking
- ❑ Roller Blading
- ❑ Wildlife viewing

Facilities:

- ❑ ADA
- ❑ Pavilions
- ❑ Picnic sites
- ❑ Playground
- ❑ Restrooms
- ❑ Visitor center
- ❑
- ❑
- ❑
- ❑
- ❑

Get the Facts

- ❑ Phone   352-466-3397
- ❑ Park Hours

_____

- ❑ Distance from home

  miles: _____

  hours: _____

- ❑ Address or GPS

_____

_____

Date visited:

I went with:
_____

My favorite things:
_____

_____

_____

Fees:

- ❑ Day Use $ _____
- ❑ Parking $_____
- ❑ Refund policy

_____

_____

Notes

Nature Coast State Trail
City: Fanning Springs   County: Gilchrist

Plan your trip https://www.floridastateparks.org/parks-and-trails/nature-coast-state-trail

Activities:

- ❑ Biking / Mountain
- ❑ Birding
- ❑ Boating
- ❑ Fishing
- ❑ Geo-Seeking
- ❑ Hiking
- ❑ Horseback Riding
- ❑ Paddling
- ❑ Picnicking
- ❑ Roller Blading
- ❑ Wildlife viewing

Facilities:

- ❑ ADA
- ❑ Pavilions
- ❑ Picnic sites
- ❑ Playground
- ❑ Restrooms
- ❑ Visitor center
- ❑
- ❑
- ❑
- ❑
- ❑

Get the Facts

- ❑ Phone   352-535-5181
- ❑ Park Hours

  _____

- ❑ Distance from home

  miles: _____

  hours: _____
- ❑ Address or GPS

  _____

  _____

Fees:

- ❑ Day Use $ _____
- ❑ Parking $_____
- ❑ Refund policy

  _____

  _____

Date visited:

I went with:
_____

My favorite things:
_____

_____

_____

Notes

Tallahassee-St. Marks Historic Railroad State Trail
City: Crawfordville   County: Wakulla

Plan your trip https://www.floridastateparks.org/parks-and-trails/tallahassee-st-marks-historic-railroad-state-trail

Activities:

- ❑ Biking / Mountain
- ❑ Birding
- ❑ Boating
- ❑ Fishing
- ❑ Geo-Seeking
- ❑ Hiking
- ❑ Horseback Riding
- ❑ Paddling
- ❑ Picnicking
- ❑ Roller Blading
- ❑ Wildlife viewing

Facilities:

- ❑ ADA
- ❑ Pavilions
- ❑ Picnic sites
- ❑ Playground
- ❑ Restrooms
- ❑ Visitor center
- ❑
- ❑
- ❑
- ❑
- ❑

Get the Facts

- ❑ Phone   850-487-7989
- ❑ Park Hours

  _____

- ❑ Distance from home

  miles: _____

  hours: _____

- ❑ Address or GPS

  _____

  _____

Fees:

- ❑ Day Use $ _____
- ❑ Parking $_____
- ❑ Refund policy

  _____

  _____

Date visited:

I went with:

_____

My favorite things:

_____

_____

_____

Notes

Palatka-to-Lake Butler State Trail
City: Keystone Heights   County: Clay

Plan your trip https://www.floridastateparks.org/parks-and-trails/palatka-lake-butler-state-trail

Activities:

- ❏ Biking / Mountain
- ❏ Birding
- ❏ Boating
- ❏ Fishing
- ❏ Geo-Seeking
- ❏ Hiking
- ❏ Horseback Riding
- ❏ Paddling
- ❏ Picnicking
- ❏ Roller Blading
- ❏ Wildlife viewing

Facilities:

- ❏ ADA
- ❏ Pavilions
- ❏ Picnic sites
- ❏ Playground
- ❏ Restrooms
- ❏ Visitor center
- ❏
- ❏
- ❏
- ❏
- ❏

Get the Facts

- ❏ Phone   352-473-4701
- ❏ Park Hours

  _____

- ❏ Distance from home

  miles: _____

  hours: _____

- ❏ Address or GPS

  _____

  _____

Date visited:

I went with:

_____

My favorite things:

_____

_____

_____

Fees:

- ❏ Day Use $ _____
- ❏ Parking $_____
- ❏ Refund policy

  _____

  _____

Notes

Palatka to St. Augustine State Trail
City: Elkton   County: St. Johns

Plan your trip https://www.floridastateparks.org/parks-and-trails/palatka-st-augustine-state-trail

Activities:

- ❏ Biking / Mountain
- ❏ Birding
- ❏ Boating
- ❏ Fishing
- ❏ Geo-Seeking
- ❏ Hiking
- ❏ Horseback Riding
- ❏ Paddling
- ❏ Picnicking
- ❏ Roller Blading
- ❏ Wildlife viewing

Facilities:

- ❏ ADA
- ❏ Pavilions
- ❏ Picnic sites
- ❏ Playground
- ❏ Restrooms
- ❏ Visitor center
- ❏
- ❏
- ❏
- ❏
- ❏

Get the Facts

- ❏ Phone   386-329-3721
- ❏ Park Hours

_____

- ❏ Distance from home

miles: _____

hours: _____

- ❏ Address or GPS

_____

_____

Date visited:

I went with:

_____

My favorite things:

_____

_____

_____

Fees:

- ❏ Day Use $ _____
- ❏ Parking $_____
- ❏ Refund policy

_____

_____

Notes

Withlacoochee State Trail
City: Ocala   County: Marion

Plan your trip https://www.floridastateparks.org/parks-and-trails/withlacoochee-bay-trail

Activities:

- ❑ Biking / Mountain
- ❑ Birding
- ❑ Boating
- ❑ Fishing
- ❑ Geo-Seeking
- ❑ Hiking
- ❑ Horseback Riding
- ❑ Paddling
- ❑ Picnicking
- ❑ Roller Blading
- ❑ Wildlife viewing

Facilities:

- ❑ ADA
- ❑ Pavilions
- ❑ Picnic sites
- ❑ Playground
- ❑ Restrooms
- ❑ Visitor center
- ❑
- ❑
- ❑
- ❑
- ❑

Get the Facts

- ❑ Phone   352-347-1163
- ❑ Park Hours

_____

- ❑ Distance from home

  miles: _____

  hours: _____

- ❑ Address or GPS

_____

_____

Fees:

- ❑ Day Use $ _____
- ❑ Parking $_____
- ❑ Refund policy

_____

_____

Date visited:

I went with:

_____

My favorite things:

_____

_____

_____

Notes

Dunnellon Trail
City: Dunnellon   County: Marion

Plan your trip https://www.floridastateparks.org/parks-and-trails/dunnellon-trail

Activities:

- ❑ Biking / Mountain
- ❑ Birding
- ❑ Boating
- ❑ Fishing
- ❑ Geo-Seeking
- ❑ Hiking
- ❑ Horseback Riding
- ❑ Paddling
- ❑ Picnicking
- ❑ Roller Blading
- ❑ Wildlife viewing

Facilities:

- ❑ ADA
- ❑ Pavilions
- ❑ Picnic sites
- ❑ Playground
- ❑ Restrooms
- ❑ Visitor center
- ❑
- ❑
- ❑
- ❑
- ❑

Get the Facts

- ❑ Phone   352-236-7143
- ❑ Park Hours

_____

- ❑ Distance from home

miles: _____

hours: _____

- ❑ Address or GPS

_____

_____

Date visited:

I went with:

_____

My favorite things:

_____

_____

_____

Fees:

- ❑ Day Use $ _____
- ❑ Parking $_____
- ❑ Refund policy

_____

_____

Notes

Baseline Road Trailhead
City: Ocala   County: Marion

Plan your trip https://www.floridastateparks.org/parks-and-trails/baseline-road-trailhead

Activities:

- ❑ Biking / Mountain
- ❑ Birding
- ❑ Boating
- ❑ Fishing
- ❑ Geo-Seeking
- ❑ Hiking
- ❑ Horseback Riding
- ❑ Paddling
- ❑ Picnicking
- ❑ Roller Blading
- ❑ Wildlife viewing

Facilities:

- ❑ ADA
- ❑ Pavilions
- ❑ Picnic sites
- ❑ Playground
- ❑ Restrooms
- ❑ Visitor center
- ❑
- ❑
- ❑
- ❑
- ❑
- ❑

Get the Facts

- ❑ Phone   352-671-8560
- ❑ Park Hours

  _____

- ❑ Distance from home

  miles: _____

  hours: _____

- ❑ Address or GPS

  _____

  _____

Date visited:

I went with:

_____

My favorite things:

_____

_____

_____

Notes

Fees:

- ❑ Day Use $ _____
- ❑ Parking $_____
- ❑ Refund policy

  _____

  _____

Landbridge Trail
City: Ocala　　　　County: Marion

Plan your trip https://www.floridastateparks.org/parks-and-trails/landbridge-trailhead

Activities:

- ❑ Biking / Mountain
- ❑ Birding
- ❑ Boating
- ❑ Fishing
- ❑ Geo-Seeking
- ❑ Hiking
- ❑ Horseback Riding
- ❑ Paddling
- ❑ Picnicking
- ❑ Roller Blading
- ❑ Wildlife viewing

Facilities:

- ❑ ADA
- ❑ Pavilions
- ❑ Picnic sites
- ❑ Playground
- ❑ Restrooms
- ❑ Visitor center
- ❑
- ❑
- ❑
- ❑
- ❑

Get the Facts

- ❑ Phone   352-236-7143
- ❑ Park Hours

  _____

- ❑ Distance from home

  miles: _____

  hours: _____
- ❑ Address or GPS

  _____

  _____

Date visited:

I went with:

_____

My favorite things:

_____

_____

_____

Fees:

- ❑ Day Use $ _____
- ❑ Parking $_____
- ❑ Refund policy

  _____

  _____

Notes

General James A. Van Fleet State Trail
City: Polk City   County: Polk

Plan your trip https://www.floridastateparks.org/index.php/parks-and-trails/general-james-van-fleet-state-trail

Activities:

- ❏ Biking / Mountain
- ❏ Birding
- ❏ Boating
- ❏ Fishing
- ❏ Geo-Seeking
- ❏ Hiking
- ❏ Horseback Riding
- ❏ Paddling
- ❏ Picnicking
- ❏ Roller Blading
- ❏ Wildlife viewing

Facilities:

- ❏ ADA
- ❏ Pavilions
- ❏ Picnic sites
- ❏ Playground
- ❏ Restrooms
- ❏ Visitor center
- ❏
- ❏
- ❏
- ❏
- ❏

Get the Facts

- ❏ Phone   352-394-3969
- ❏ Park Hours

  _____

- ❏ Distance from home

  miles: _____

  hours: _____
- ❏ Address or GPS

  _____

  _____

Fees:

- ❏ Day Use $ _____
- ❏ Parking $_____
- ❏ Refund policy

  _____

  _____

Date visited:

I went with:

_____

My favorite things:

_____

_____

_____

Notes

Florida Keys Overseas Heritage Trail
City: Key Largo   County: Monroe

Plan your trip https://www.floridastateparks.org/index.php/parks-and-trails/florida-keys-overseas-heritage-trail

Activities:

- ❑ Biking / Mountain
- ❑ Birding
- ❑ Boating
- ❑ Fishing
- ❑ Geo-Seeking
- ❑ Hiking
- ❑ Horseback Riding
- ❑ Paddling
- ❑ Picnicking
- ❑ Roller Blading
- ❑ Wildlife viewing

Facilities:

- ❑ ADA
- ❑ Pavilions
- ❑ Picnic sites
- ❑ Playground
- ❑ Restrooms
- ❑ Visitor center
- ❑
- ❑
- ❑
- ❑
- ❑

Get the Facts

- ❑ Phone   305-853-3571
- ❑ Park Hours

_____

- ❑ Distance from home

miles: _____

hours: _____

- ❑ Address or GPS

_____

_____

Fees:

- ❑ Day Use $ _____
- ❑ Parking $_____
- ❑ Refund policy

_____

_____

Date visited:

I went with:

_____

My favorite things:

_____

_____

_____

Notes

INDEX

INDEX